Wise Publications
London/New York/Sydney/Cologne

Exclusive Distributors:
Music Sales Limited
78 Newman Street, London W1P 3LA, England
Music Sales Pty. Limited
27 Clarendon Street, Ararmon, Sydney, NSW 2064, Australia

UK ISBN 0.7119.0491.X
UK Order No. AM36450

Art direction by Howard Brown
Cover and title pages embroidered by Sally Geeve
Compiled by Peter Evans

Printed in England by
The Anchor Press Limited, Tiptree, Essex.

EARLY FAVOURITES

SHOWTUNES

BIG BANDS

CLASSICAL THEMES

INTERNATIONAL SONGS

ROCK 'N' ROLL

FILM MUSIC

POP MUSIC

GIRLS' NAMES

LOVE SONGS

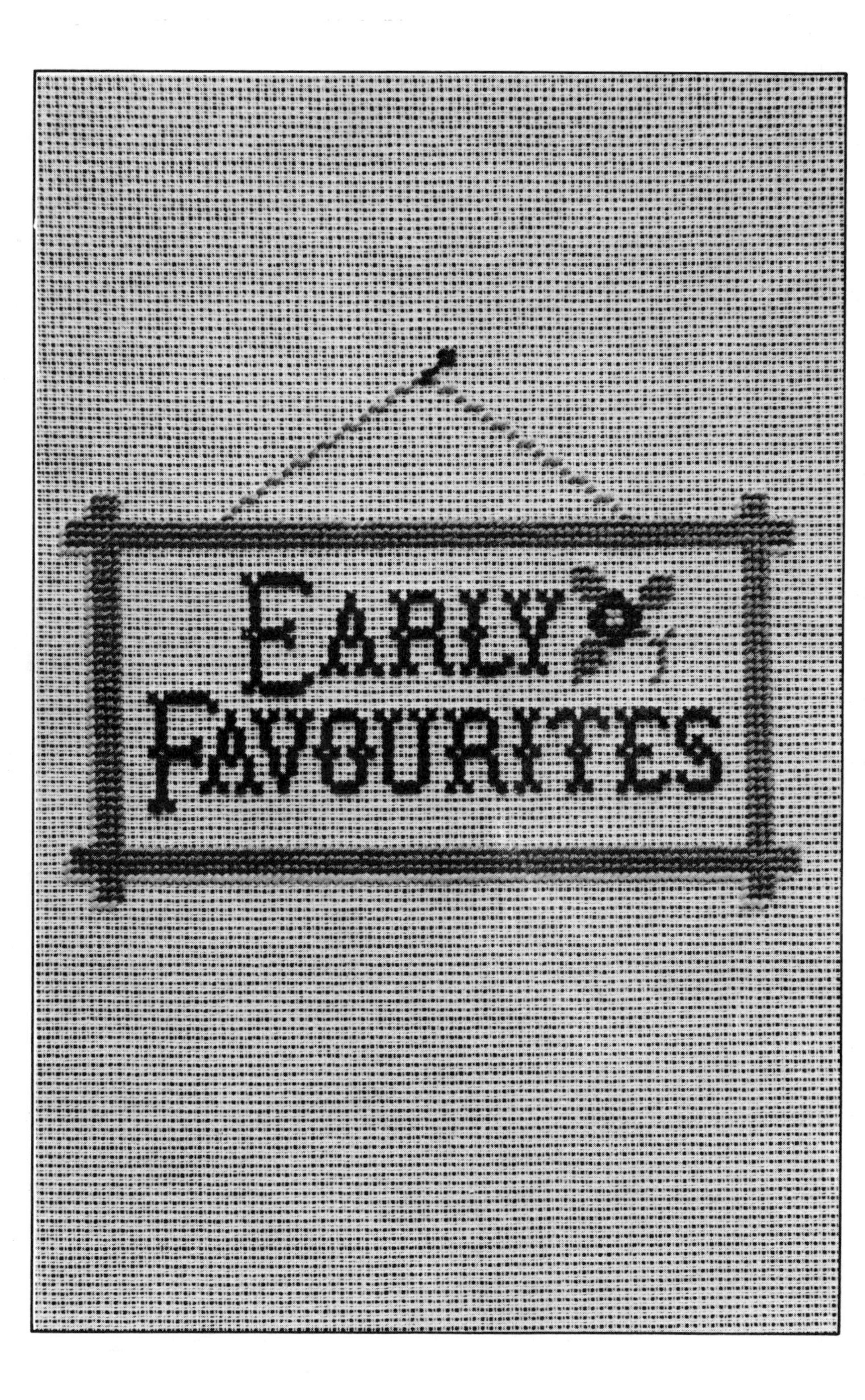
EARLY
FAVOURITES

FRANKIE AND JOHNNY

Traditional

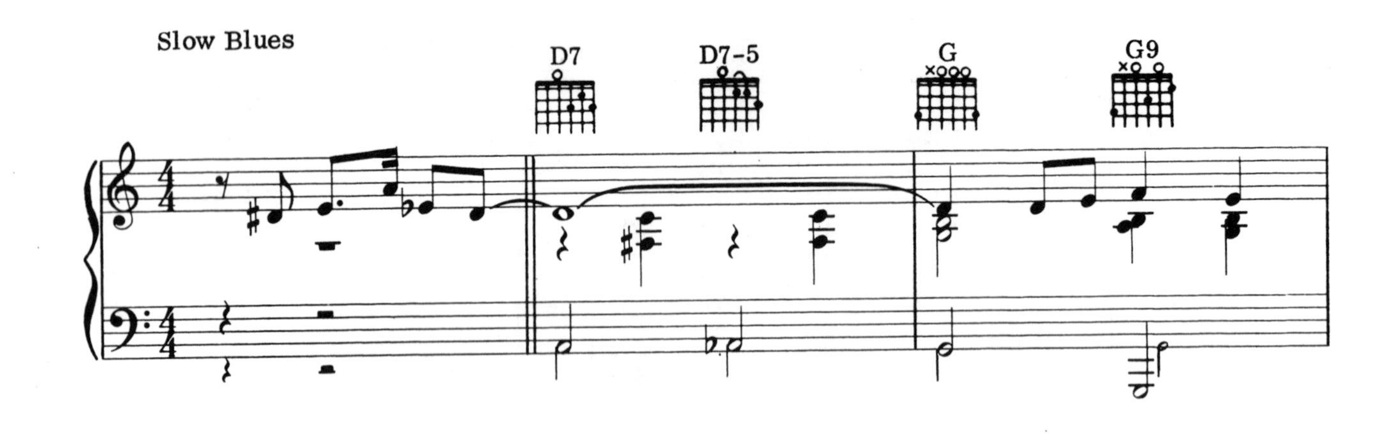

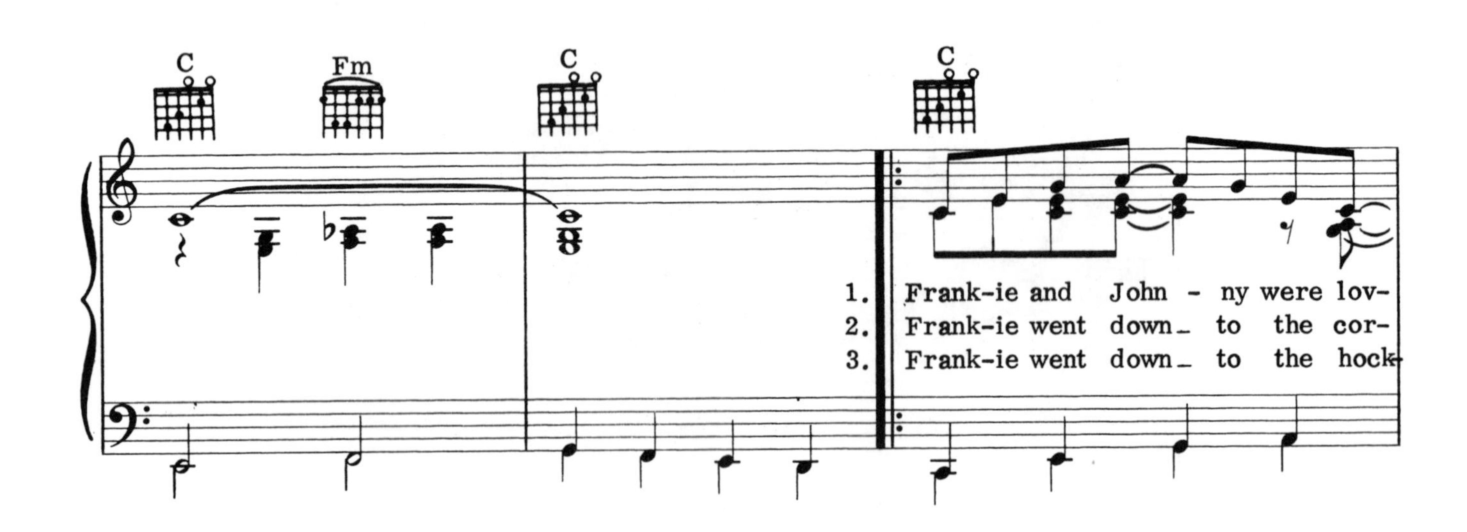

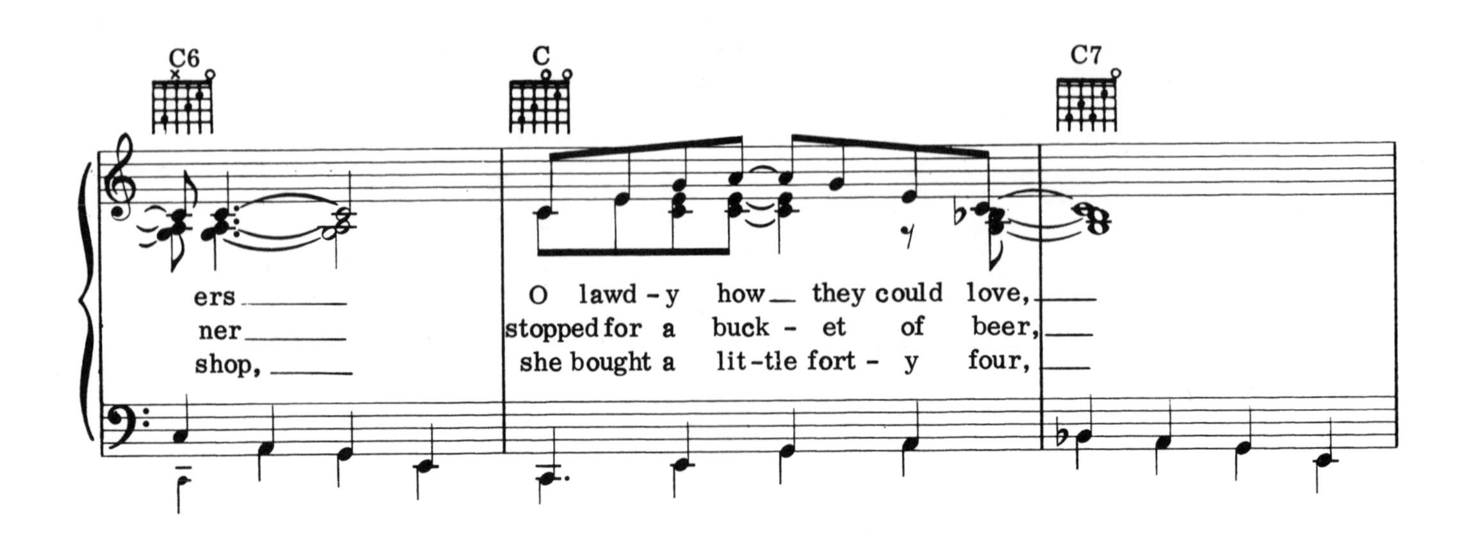

F
F♯o7
Swore to be true _ to each oth - er, ___ true as the stars a - bove,
she said "O Mis - ter bar tend - er, ___ has my John - ny been here?
she aimed it at _ the ceil - ing, ___ and shot a hole in the _
C
C6
C♯o7
G
G9
last time to ending
3
he was her man _ but he done her
He was my man _ but he done me
floor." Where is my man _ he's do - in' me
C
Fm
C
C
wrong. ___
wrong." ___
wrong. ___
Frank-ie and John - ny went walk -
Now I ain't gon - na tell no sto -
Frank-ie went down to the ho -
C6
C
C7
ing, ___ John - ny in his _ bran' new suit, ___
ry, ___ ain't gon - na tell _ you no lie, ___
tel, ___ she rang that _ ho - tel bell, ___

F
"O good lawd says Frank - ie,
John - ny was here an hour a - go,
"Stand back all of you chip - pies,
F#o7
C
C#o7
"Don't my John- ny look cute?"
He was her man
with a gal named Nel - lie Bly,
he was your man
I'll blow you all to hell
I wan my man
G
G9
1-6. C
Fm
but he done her wrong.
but he's do - in' you wrong.
he's do - in' me wrong.
C
7. C
Fm
C
C6
wrong.

4. Frankie looked over the tron som,
   And there to her great surprise,
   Yes, there on the bed sat Johnny,
   Makin' love to Nellie Bly,
   He was her man but he done her wrong.
   Frankie threw back her kimono,
   She took out the little forty-four,
   Roota-toot-toot, three times she shot,
   Right through that hard wood door,
   She shot her man, because he done her wrong.

5. Johnny he grabbed off his stetson,
   "Omy gawd, Frankie, don't shoot,"
   But Frankie put her finger on the trigger,
   Once again that roota-toot-toot,
   For he was her man and he done her wrong.
   O roll me over easy,
   O roll me over slow,
   Roll me on my right side, honey,
   Where the bullets ain't hurtin' me so,
   You've shot your man 'cause he done you wrong.

6. Bring out your rubber-tired hearses,
   Bring out your rubber-tired hack,
   There's twelve men goin' to the graveyard,
   And eleven coming back,
   He was my man, but he done me wrong.
   O, bring 'round a thousand policemen,
   Bring 'em around today,
   To lock me in that dungeon.
   And throw the key away,
   I shot my man, 'cause he done me wrong.

7. I've saved up a little bit of money,
   I'll save up a little bit more,
   I'll send it all to his widow,
   And say it's from the woman next door,
   He was my man, but he done me wrong.
   Frankie she said to the Warden,
   "What are they goin' to do?"
   The Warden he said to Frankie,
   "It's the sizzlin' hot chair for you,
   You shot your man, though he done you wrong."

8. This story has no moral,
   This story has no end,
   This story only goes to show,
   That there ain't no good in men,
   He was her man, and he done her wrong.

BILL BAILEY WON'T YOU PLEASE COME HOME

Traditional

D+5
G
Am7
D7
I knows I've done you wrong.
G
'Mem-ber dat rain - y eve dat I drove you out wid
G7
C
E7/B
Am
Am7
noth-ing but a fine tooth comb?
I knows I'se to
Am7-5/C
G
E7
A7
blame; well ain't dat a shame? Bill Bai-ley, won't you
Cm/E♭
3fr.
D7
G
Am
D7
G6
please come home?

AIN'T SHE SWEET

Words: Jack Yellen
Music: Milton Ager

CHORUS
Ain't she sweet? See her coming down the street! Now I ask you very con-fi-den-tial-ly ain't she
p-f
Cm C#dim Bb7 Cm C#dim Bb7 Eb G7 C7 F7 Bb7
sweet? Ain't she nice? Look her ov-er once or twice. Now I ask you ve-ry con-fi-den-tial-ly
Eb Bb Cm C#dim Bb7 Cm C#dim Bb7 Eb G7 C7
ain't she nice? Just cast an eye in her di-rec-tion Oh, me! Oh, my!
F7 Bb7 Eb Eb7 Ab7 Eb Eb7 Ab7
Ain't that per-fec-tion? I re-peat don't you think that's kind of
Eb Fm Bb7 Cm C#dim Bb7 Cm C#dim
1 2 D.S.
neat? And I ask you ve-ry con-fi-den-tial-ly Ain't she sweet? sweet?
Bb7 Eb G7 C7 F7 Bb7 Eb Edim Bb7 Eb Ab7 Eb

IF I HAD MY WAY

Words: Lou Klein
Music: James Kendis

A7 D7 G7 C E7 F Ab7
ros - es for you and for me. A thous-and and one things, dear, I would
C D7 G7 C
optional
do Just for you, Just for you, on - ly you. IF I HAD MY
A7 D7 G7 C E7 F A7
WAY, we would nev - er grow old, And sun-shine I'd bring ev - 'ry day.
Dm Cdim C A7 D7
— You would reign all a - lone Like a queen on a throne, IF I HAD
cresc
G7 C C
MY WAY. If WAY.

CAROLINA MOON

Words: Benny Davis
Music: Joe Burke

Won't some-bo-dy tell the moon for me, Oh!
Shi - ning on the same old wind-ing lane, Oh!
rit.
A7 D7 D+
CHORUS Dreamily
Car - o-li - na moon keep shi - ning, Shi - ning on the
G C Cm G
one who waits for me,
Car - o - li - na moon I'm
D7 G Go G G
pi - ning Pi - ning for the place I long to be.
C Cm G D7 G

3
How I'm hop-ing to-night you'll go, Go to the right win - dow
G7 C G
scat-ter your light, Say I'm al - right please do,
A7 D7 D7+
Tell her that I'm blue and lone - ly, Dream-y Car - o -
G C Cm G
li - na moon. moon.
1 2
A7 ♭5 D7 G D7 D7+ G
D. C.

ON THE SUNNY SIDE OF THE STREET

Words: Dorothy Fields
Music: Jimmy McHugh

Chorus
Grab your coat, and get your hat, Leave your wor - ry on the door - step,
mp-mf
C
E7
F
Em
Just di - rect your feet To the sun - ny side of the street. Can't you
3
Am E7 Am Cm D7
F Dm
C
hear a pit - ter - pat? And that hap - py tune is your step, Life can be so
C
E7
F
Em
Am E7 Am E7
sweet, On the sun - ny side of the street, I used to walk in the shade
D7
F Dm
C
C7

With those blues on par - ade But I'm not a - fraid
F6
D7
This ro - ver crossed o - ver, If I ne-ver have a cent I'll be
G7
C
E7
rich as Rock- e - fel - ler, Gold dust at my feet, On the
F
Em
Am E7 Am Cm D7
sun - ny side of the street. Grab your street.
F
Dm
C
C
sfz
D.C.

ON A SLOW BOAT TO CHINA

Words & Music: Frank Loesser

Cm
C#dim
B♭
D7
E♭
Cm
moon big and shin - y,
Melt - ing your heart of stone,
Fm
G7
Cm7
A♭7
A7
B♭
A♭7
G+
G7
I'd love to get you ON A SLOW BOAT TO CHI - NA,
C7
Cm7
B7
1
B♭
Cm7
F9+
All to my - self a - lone.
2 To Interlude
B♭
lone.
There is no
3 Fine
B♭
Cm7
F7+5 -9
B♭
lone.
mf
ff
Interlude
B♭
E♭
E dim
B♭
E dim
E♭ Cm7
F7
Back to Chorus
verse to this song, 'Cause I don't want to wait a mo-ment too long To say that

AMAPOLA

Words: Albert Gamse
Music: Joseph M. Lacalle

CHORUS
Bb
Ddim
A-MA - PO - LA, my pretty lit-tle pop - py, You're like that love-ly flow'r so sweet and
p
f a tempo
F7
heav-en-ly Since I found you, My heart is wrapp'd a-round you, And loving you,it seems to
F7+
Bb
beat a rhap-so-dy. A-MA-PO - LA, the pret-ty lit-tle pop - py must cop-y its en-
G7
Cm
G7
Cm
Ebm
Bb
-dear - ing charm from you. A-MA-PO - LA, A-MA-PO - LA,
C7
F7
1
Bb
2
Bb
How I long to hear you say I love you. A-MA- love you.
poco rall.
fz
D.S.

I CAN'T GIVE YOU ANYTHING BUT LOVE

Words: Dorothy Fields
Music: Jimmy McHugh

CHORUS
I can't give you an-y-thing but love Ba - by, That's the only thing I've plen-ty of
mp-f
G Gdim Am7 D7 G Gdim Am7
Ba - by, Dream a while, scheme a while, We're sure to find Hap-pi-ness
D7 Gmaj7 G7 C Am A7
and I guess All those things you've always pined for, Gee, I'd like to see you looking swell, Ba - by,
D7 B♭7 A♭m C7 D7 G Gdim Am7 D7
Dia-mond brace-lets Wool-worth doesn't sell, Ba-by, Till that lu-cky day, you know darn well,
G7 Cmaj7 Am7 C A7 D7
1 2 D.C.
Ba- by, I can't give you an-y-thing but love. love.
rit. a tempo allarg. fz
E7 Am7 Em7 Am7 D7 G Gdim C Am G Cm G

BURLINGTON BERTIE FROM BOW

Words & Music: William Hargreaves

Jog-ging a - long, heart-y and strong, liv-ing on plates of fresh
Call for Cham-pagne, walk out a-gain, come back and bor-row the
cheer up-on cheer, When I ap-pear— Cap-tain with my Po-lo
holds up my face, keeps it in place, stops it from slip-ping a-
Emi B7 E7 Ami B7 Ami
air, I dress up in fash-ion, and,
ink, I live most ex-pen-sive, like
team, So strict are my peo-ple, they're
-way, Ci-gars I smoke thou-sands, I
B7 Emi B7 Emi B7 Emi B7 Emi B7
when I am feel-ing de-press'd, I shave from my cuff all the
Tom Lip-ton I'm in the swim, He's got so much 'oof,' that he
Wil-liam the Con-quer-or's strain, If they ev-er knew, I'd been
us-ual-ly deal in the Strand, But you've got to take care, when you're
Emi B7 Emi B7
whis-kers and fluff, stick my hat on and tod-dle up West.
sleeps on the roof, and I live in the room ov-er him.
talk-ing to you why, they'd nev-er look at me a-gain.
get-ting them there or some id-iot might stand on your hand.
Emi B7 A7 Am7 ♭5 D7

CHORUS.

I'm Bur-ling-ton Ber-tie, I rise at ten thir-ty and saun-ter a-
I'm Bur-ling-ton Ber-tie, I rise at ten thir-ty then saun-ter a-
I'm Bur-ling-ton Ber-tie, I rise at ten thir-ty and reach Kemp-ton
I'm Bur-ling-ton Ber-tie, I rise at ten thir-ty then Buck-ing-ham
G
-long like a toff, I walk down the Strand with my
-long Tem-ple Bar, As round there I skip, I keep
Park a-bout three, I stand by the rail, when a
pal-ace, I view; I stand in the yard while they're
C
E7
Ami
fz
gloves on my hand, then I walk down a-gain with them off,
shout-ing "Pip! Pip!" and the darn'd fools think I'm in my car,
horse is for sale, and you ought to see Woo-ton watch me,
chang-ing the guard, and the King shouts a-cross "Too-dle-oo;"
D7
I'm all airs and gra-ces, cor-rect ea-sy pa-ces, with-
At Roth-child's I swank it, my bo-dy I plank it on
I lean on some awn-ing, while Lord Der-by's yawn-ing, then
The Prince of Wales' bro-ther, a-long with some oth-er, slaps
G
Cmi
G

-out food so long I've for - got where my face is— I'm Bert,
his front door - step with "the Mail" for a blan - ket, I'm Bert,
he bids "Two Thou - sand," and I bid "good morn - ing," I'm Bert,
me on the back, and says "come and see mo - ther," I'm Bert,
D7 G7 C Cmi D7 G D7 G D7 G
Bert, I have - n't a shirt, but my peo - ple are well off, you
Bert, and Roth - child was hurt, He said, "You can't sleep there I said
Bert, I'd buy one, a Cert, but___ where could I keep it, you
Bert, and Roy - al - ty's hurt, when they ask me to dine, I say
E7 D7 G
know!___ Near - ly ev - 'ry one knows me, from Smith to Lord
Oh!"___ He said I'm Roth - child son - ny!" I said, "That's damn'd
know!___ I can't let my man see me— in bed with a
"No!___ I've just had a Ba - na - na with La - dy Di -
Am7 b5 D7 G D7 G7 C D7 E7 A E7 A7
Rose - b'ry I'm Bur - ling - ton Ber - tie from Bow!"___
fun - ny I'm Bur - ling - ton Ber - tie from Bow!"___
Gee - Gee! I'm Bur - ling - ton Ber - tie from Bow!"___
-an - a, I'm Bur - ling - ton Ber - tie from Bow!"___
mf
ff
D7 Emi D7 G G#dim D7 G

I AIN'T GOT NOBODY
(and there's nobody cares for me)

Words & Music: Roger Graham
& Spencer Williams

D
G#dim
D
D#dim
A7
A7-5
D7
C
D7
D+
now I'm sad and lone - ly, for he's gone and turned me down. 'Cause
have no one to love me, no one to con - tent my mind.
CHORUS
G7
F#7
F7
E7
A7
A7-5
I ain't got no - bo - dy, And there's
p-f
G
Gm
A7
D7
G
C
Cm
G
Ddim
D
D+
G7
no - bo - dy cares for me. I'm
F#7
F7
E7
A7
A7
so sad and lone - ly, won't some-bo-dy come and take a chance with

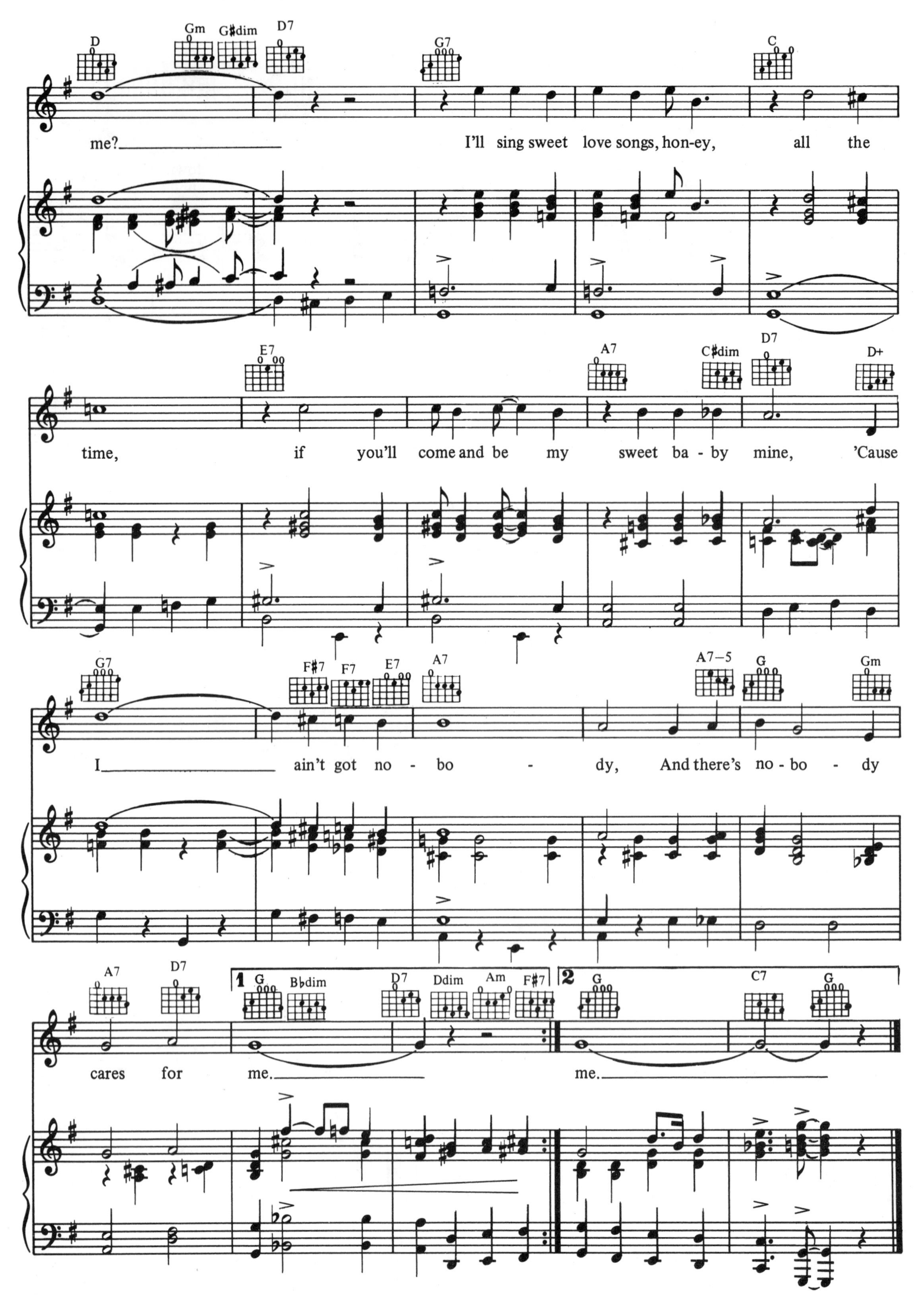
D
Gm
G♯dim
D7
G7
C
me?
I'll sing sweet love songs, hon-ey, all the
E7
A7
C♯dim
D7
D+
time, if you'll come and be my sweet ba - by mine, 'Cause
G7
F♯7
F7
E7
A7
A7−5
G
Gm
I ain't got no - bo - dy, And there's no - bo - dy
A7
D7
1
G
B♭dim
D7
Ddim
Am
F♯7
2
G
C7
G
cares for me. me.

SHOW
TUNES

GETTING TO KNOW YOU

Words: Oscar Hammerstein II
Music: Richard Rodgers

Dm7 G7 C Dm7 G7
tea! Get-ting To Know You, get-ting to feel free and eas - y
f p
Dm7 G7 Dm7 G7 Dm7 G7 C7
When I am with you, get-ting to know what to say.
Fmaj7 F6 Dm7 G7 Cmaj7 C7 F
Have-n't you not - iced? Sud-den-ly I'm bright and breez - y Be-cause of
C Dm7 G7 C Am7 D7 Am7 D7 Dm7
all the beau-ti-ful and new things I'm learn-ing a-bout you day
poco a poco cresc.
G7 C Dm7 G7 C F C
by day. Get-ting To day.
f p mf

HEY THERE

Words & Music: Richard Adler
& Jerry Ross

Bb9 Eb B7 Fm7 Bb7-9 Eb B7 Fm7 Bb9 Bb7
Bet - ter for - get her, Her with her nose in the air, She has you danc - ing
C9 Fm7/Bb Bb7 Bbm7 Eb13 E9 Eb9
on a string, Break it and she won't care! Won't you
Abmaj7 Am7-5 D7+5 D7 Gm7 C9 C7-9
take this ad - vice I hand you like a broth-er? Or are you
Fm7 Abm6 Gm7 C7 Fm Gm7
not see - ing things too clear, Are you too much in love to hear, Is it all go - ing in one
Abmaj7 Bb7-9 D/Eb Eb Fm7 Bb7 D/Eb Eb Eb6/9
ear and out the oth - er? oth - er?
cresc.
mp

CLIMB EV'RY MOUNTAIN

Words: Oscar Hammerstein II
Music: Richard Rodgers

C
F
Dm
G
C
dream! A dream that will need all the love you can give,
D7
G
Em
A
D
Ev-'ry day of your life for as long as you live.
cresc.
D7
G
A7
D
Dm7
G
Climb Ev - 'ry Moun - tain, ford ev - 'ry
f
Cmaj7
Am
Em
Dm
C
E+
stream, Fol - low ev - 'ry rain - bow till you
ff
F6
G7
1 C
Dm7
G7
2 C
find your dream!
dream!
mp
ff
mp

I DON'T KNOW HOW TO LOVE HIM

Music: Andrew Lloyd Webber
Lyrics: Tim Rice

A9sus (no G) A D G D G D
else I don't know how to take this
G G6 G D/A A D/F♯ A
I don't see why he moves me He's a man he's just a
D A F♯m7 Bm F♯m7 Bm
man And I've had so man-y men be-fore In
G D/F♯ Em D A9sus (no G) A G D/F♯ Em7 D
ver-y man-y ways He's just one more
p

G
F#7
Should I bring him down — should I scream and shout —
mp
cresc. poco
a poco
Bm
Bm/A
G
D/A
C
— Should I speak of love — let my feel-ings out? — I nev-er thought I'd
ff
G
D
G
D/F#
Em
come to this — what's it all a - bout? —
f
dim. poco a
poco
A9sus
(no G)
A
D
G
D
G
D
Don't you think it's rath-er fun - ny
Yet if he said he loved me
mp

G G6 G D/A A D/F♯ A
I should be in this po - si - tion? I'm the one who's al - ways
I'd be lost I'd be fright - ened I could - n't cope just could - n't
D A F♯m7 Bm7 F♯m7 Bm7
been So calm so cool, no lov - er's fool
cope I'd turn my head I'd back a - way I
G D/F♯ Em D A9sus (no G) A G D/F♯ Em7
1.
D
Run - ning ev - 'ry show He scares me so
would - n't want to know He scares me
p
2.
D G D/F♯ Em7 D G D/F♯ Em7 D
so I want him so I love him so
mp
mf

AS LONG AS HE NEEDS ME

Words & Music: Lionel Bart

he needs me. As long as life is long, I'll love him right or
Fm6 G7 Cmaj7 C6 G7 Cmaj7 C6 Cmaj7 C6 Cmaj7 C♯dim
wrong; And some-how I'll be strong As long as he needs me. If you are
Dm7 G7 Dm7 Dm B♭ G7 Fm6 G7 Cmaj7 C6
lone - ly then you will know When someone needs you you love them so. I won't be-
Fsus F Dm7 G7 Cmaj7 C Am7 D7 Dm7 G7
-tray his trust, Tho' peo-ple say I must. I've got to stay true,
Cmaj7 C6 Cmaj7 C6 Cmaj7 C♯dim Dm7 G7 Dm Dm7
just As long as he needs me. As long as he needs me.
mf
D9 Dm7 G9 C G7 Dm7 G7-9 C6

DIAMONDS ARE A GIRL'S BEST FRIEND

Words: Leo Robin
Music: Jule Styne

gives ex - pen - sive jew-els;
stones still keep their flick-er;
Bb Gm7 C7 F
CHORUS
A kiss on the hand may be quite Con - ti - nen-tal But
There may come a time when a lass needs a law-yer, But
C7 F Bb F C7
Dia-monds Are A Girl's Best Friend, A kiss may be
Dia-monds Are A Girl's Best Friend, There may come a
F F dim Gm6 C9b C7 B7 Gm
grand But it won't pay the rent-al on your hum-ble flat Or
time When a hard boiled em - ploy-er thinks you're aw-ful nice, But
D7 G Am7 G dim G Am7 G7

help you at the Au - to - mat. Men grow cold as girls grow
get that "ice" or else no dice. He's your guy when stocks are
mp
C9 Gm7 C9 C7 Cm Fdim F9 B♭ A
old And we all lose our charms in the end. But
high, But be - ware when they start to de - scend. It's
B♭ B♭m F A7 Dm G7 C7 F C7
square cut or pear shape, These rocks don't lose their shape, Dia - monds Are A
then that those lous - es Go back to their spous - es, Dia - monds Are A
cresc
F Cm6 Am7 D7 Gm7
1
2
Girl's Best Friend. A
Girl's Best Friend.
f
mf
f
C9♭ F Fdim C7 F C7 F B♭6 F

BIG SPENDER

Words: Dorothy Fields
Music: Cy Coleman

B♭
E7-5
I don't pop my cork for ev - 'ry guy I see.
Dm
To Coda
B♭7
A7
Hey! Big Spend-er, Spend a lit - tle time with
Dm
tacet
me.
Would-n't you like to have
D
F♯m
Bm
D
Em
B+
1st Fret
Em7
fun, fun, fun? How's a-bout a few laughs laughs? I can show you a

B♭9
A9
A13
D.𝄋. al Coda
good time, Let me show you a good time. The min-ute you
CODA
tacet
E♭m
Dm
Hey, Big Spend-er!
Hey, Big Spend-er!
Spend a lit-tle time with me,
Spend a lit-tle time with
me,
Spend a lit-tle time with me.
Dm6(add9)

IF MY FRIENDS COULD SEE ME NOW

C
C7
(1.) see me now, that lit - tle gang of mine, I'm
(2.) see me now, my lit - tle dust y group,
(3.) see me now, a - lone with Mis - ter V., Who's
F
eat - ing fan - cy chow and drink - ing fan - cy wine. I'd like those
Traip - sin' 'round this mil - lion dol - lar chick - en coop. I'd hear those
wait - in' on me like he was a mai - tre d'. I hear my
B7
E7
Am
stum - ble bums to see for a fact The kind of
thrift shop cats say: "Broth - er, get her! Draped on a
bud - dies say - ing: "Cra - zy, what gives? To - night she's
D7
Fm6
C
D7
G7
top - drawer, first - rate chums I at - tract. All I can
bed - spread made from three kinds of fur." All I can
liv - ing like the oth - er half lives." To think the

C
C7
say is, "Wow - ee! Look - a where I am. To - night I
say is, "Wow! Wait till the riff and raff See just ex -
high - est brow, which I must say is he, Should pick the
F
E7
land - ed, pow! right in a pot of jam." What a
act - ly how he signed this au - to - graph." What a
low - est brow, which there's no doubt is me. What a
A7+
B♭9
G7
A7
D7
tacet
set up! Ho - ly cow!
build - up! Ho - ly cow!
step up! Ho - ly cow!
They'd nev - er be - lieve it, If my
G7
G♯dim
F/A
G7
C
1.2.
3.
friends could see me now!
2. If they could
3. If they could

HELLO, YOUNG LOVERS

Words: Oscar Hammerstein II
Music: Richard Rodgers

Fm G7 E♭ G7 Dm7
Cling ver - y close to each oth - er to - night I've been in
G7 C F C7sus F
love like you. I know how it feels to have wings on your
mf
mp
C7sus F C7sus C7 F Dm6 E7
heels, And to fly down a street in a trance. You fly down a
Am Dm7
street on a chance that you'll meet, And you meet not real - ly by chance.

G7 C
Don't cry, young lov - ers, What - ev - er you do, Don't cry be -
G7 Fm G7 Eb G7
cause I'm a - lone.
All of my mem - 'ries are hap - py to - night
Dm7 G7 F G7 C7 F Fm C+ C6
I've had a love of my own,
I've had a love of my own like
Dm Eb G7 C G7 C
yours, I've had a love of my own. Hel - own.
p
mf
cresc. ed allargando
a tempo
f

SWEET CHARITY

Words: Dorothy Fields
Music: Cy Coleman

F
(vocal counter-melody)
G
G♭
F
G♭6
G♭7
Sweet
Cha - ri - ty,
Sweet
Cha - ri - ty,
F
G7
G♭
F
Be
good to me,
Sweet
Cha - ri - ty.
Bm7
E7+
Am
A♭m7
D♭7+
G♭m
C♭7
C7
Fmaj9
Mmm
Sweet
B♭6
Fmaj7
Cha - ri - ty,
Be
good to me,
Sweet
Cha - ri - ty,
B♭6
C7
F6
Be
good to me
to - day.

WHAT KIND OF FOOL AM I

Words & Music: Leslie Bricusse
& Anthony Newley

What kind of lips are these That lied with ev - 'ry kiss? That whis-pered
What kind of clown am I? What do I know of life? Why can't I
G13 Cmaj9 C6 Cmaj9 C♯dim Dm9 Dm7 G7 G13 G7
emp - ty words of love that left me a - lone like this Why can't I fall in love
cast a-way the mask of play and live my life? Why can't I fall in love
Em7 Em11 Gm6 A7 A7+♭9 A9+ F6
like an - y oth - er man
till I don't give a damn
And may-be then I'll know what kind of fool I
B♭9 C D7 Dm7 Fm6
1
2
am. What kind of am.
C D♭7 G9 C A♭ B♭ C

SUNRISE SUNSET

Words: Sheldon Harnick
Music: Jerry Bock

D7(-9 +5)
Gm
D7
Gm
they? side.
When did she get to be a beau-
Place the gold ring a-round her fin-
D7
Gm
G7
ty? When did he grow to be so tall?
ger, Share the sweet wine and break the glass;
Cm
G7
Cm
A7
Was-n't it yes-ter-day when they were
Soon the full cir-cle will have come to
D
D7
D6
D7
small.
pass.
8va
rit.

Chorus
Gm
Cm6
Gm
D7
SUN - RISE, SUN - SET, SUN - RISE, SUN - SET,
mp - mf
a tempo
Cm7
Cm
G7
Swift - ly flow the days; Seed - lings turn
F7
Bbmaj7
Bb6
Am7
o - ver-night to sun - flow'rs, Blos - som - ing e - ven as we
gaze. SUN - RISE, SUN - SET,

Gm Cm6 Gm D7 Gm Cm6 Gm Cm
SUN - RISE, SUN - SET, Swift - ly fly the
Gm G7 Cm6 D7-9
years; One sea - son fol - low - ing an -
Gm C7 Cm6 D7 D7+5
oth - er, Lad - en with hap - pi - ness and
1. Gm 2. Gm
tears. tears.
rit.

DON'T CRY FOR ME ARGENTINA

Music: Andrew Lloyd Webber
Lyrics: Tim Rice

you.
2. I had to let it hap - pen, I had to change; Could-n't stay all my life down at
3. And as for for - tune, and as for fame; I nev - er in - vi - ted them
G C F/C
heel: Look-ing out of the win - dow, stay - ing out of the sun. So I chose
in: Though it seemed to the world they were all I de - sired. They are il -
G7/C C Cma7
free - dom Run-ning a - round try - ing ev - ry - thing new, but no- thing im- pressed me at
- lu sions They're not the so - lu - tions they prom-ised to be, the an - swer was here all the
Am/C D7 D/C
REFRAIN
all, I nev - er ex - pect - ed it to.
time, I love you, and hope you love me.
Don't cry for me Ar - gen - ti - na the
Slow tango feel
poco rall.
G/B D7 G C

3
truth is I nev - er left you: All through my wild days, my mad ex - ist - ence, I kept my
G
To Coda
1
2 Colla voce
prom-ise, Don't keep your dis - tance.
Have I said too much? Theres
p
Fma7
Fma7
F6
F
Fma7
no - thing more I can think of to say to you
But all you have to do is
Em7
Fma7
D. S. al Coda
CODA
look at me to know that ev - ry word is true.
rall.
C
Fma7
F6
C

BIG
BAND
MUSIC

SOLITUDE

Words: Eddie de Lange & Irving Mills
Music: Duke Ellington

C Fm C Dm7 Cdim C9 F F#dim
die. I sit in my chair, I'm filled with des-pair, There's
rhythm
C G9 C9 F F#dim
no one could be so sad With gloom ev-'ry-where I sit and I stare, I
C C#dim Dm7 G7+5 Cmaj7 Cdim
know that I'll soon go mad. In my Sol-i-tude I'm
rubato
Dm7 D9 D7 G7sus4 G6 G7
pray-ing, Dear Lord a-bove send back my
1. C Cdim Dm7 G7+5
love. In my
2. C F Fm C6
love.
molto rit.

MOONGLOW

Words & Music: Will Hudson, Eddie De Lange & Irving Mills

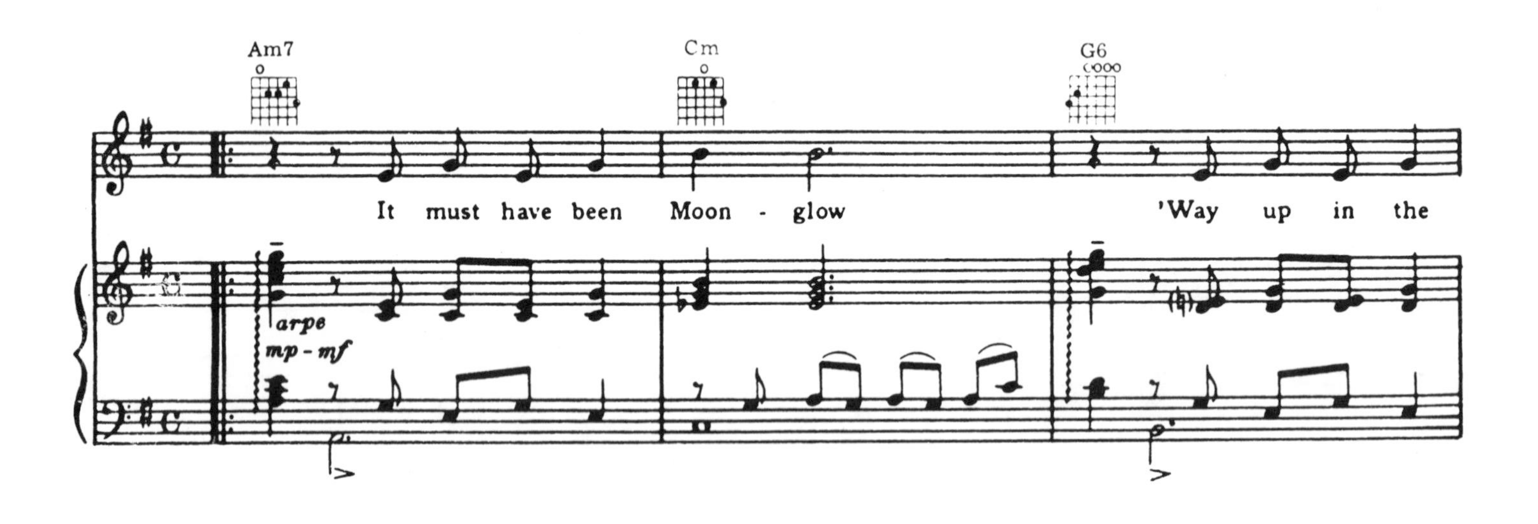

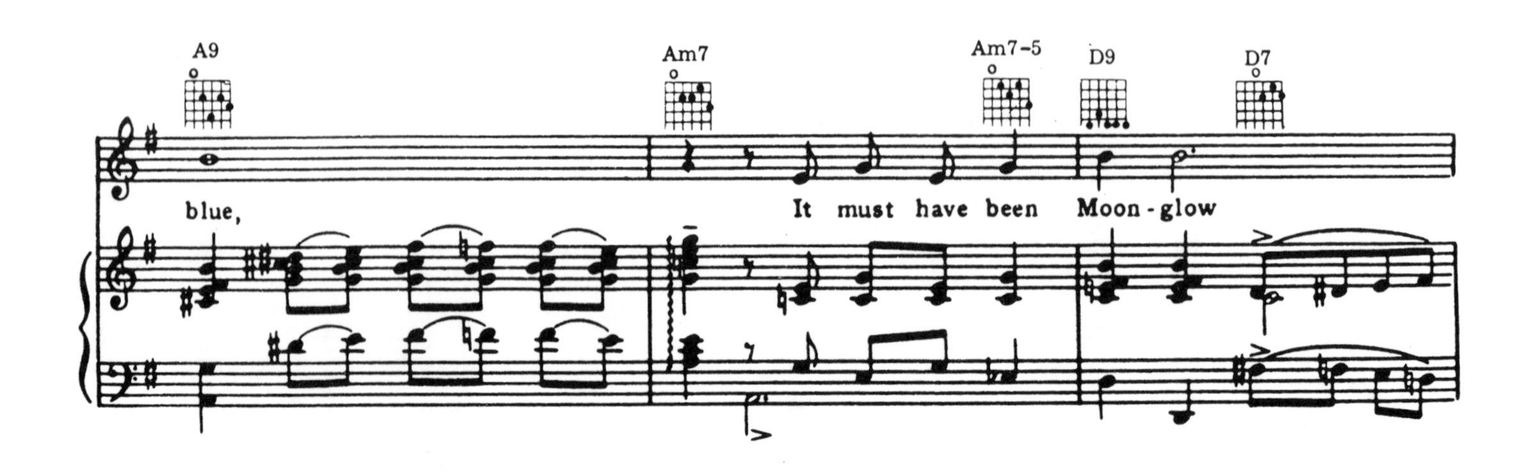

G
Eb7
Am7
Eb7
G
Am7
that led me straight to you
I still hear you
Cm
G6
A9
say - ing "Dear one, hold me fast."
Am7
Am7-5
D9
D7
G
Eb7
And I start in pray - ing Oh Lord, please
Am7
Eb7
G
G9
G7
G9
F#9
F9
let this last.
We seemed to float right thru the

E9
E
E9
A9
Am7-5
air,
Heav-en-ly songs
seemed to come from
D9
Eb9
D9
Am7
Cm
ev - 'ry - where:
And now when there's Moon-glow
G6
A9
Am7
Am7-5
'Way up in the blue,
I al-ways re-
D9
D7
1.
G
Eb7
Am7
Eb7
G
D7
mem-ber
That Moon-glow gave me you.
2.
G
Eb7
Am7
Am7-5
G
C
Cm
Gmaj7
That Moon-glow gave me you.
allargando
accel.

THE VERY THOUGHT OF YOU

Words & Music: Ray Noble

Fm7
Abm6
Bb9
Bb7
Bbm7
Eb7
For sleep - ing or wak - ing, dear, I find;
I'll on - ly be sat - is - fied with you;
poco rit.
REFRAIN
Ab
Ab6
The ver - y thought of you, And I for - get to do,
p-mf
Ab6
Ab
Bb7
The lit - tle or - di - na - ry things that ev'ry-one ought to do.
Bb7
Db
Eb7
Fm
Fm7
I'm liv - ing in a kind of day-dream, I'm hap - py as a
G7+
G7
Cm
Abm
Bb7
Bbm7
king, And fool - ish tho' it may seem, To me that's ev' - ry-

Eb7
Ab
Ab6
thing. The mere i-dea of you, The long-ing here for you,
Ab6
Ab
Bb7
You'll nev-er know how slow the mo-ments go 'till I'm near to you,
Bb7
Db
Eb7
Fm
I see your face in ev-'ry flow-er; Your
Fm
Ddim
Eb7
Adim
eyes in stars a-bove, It's just the thought of you, The ver-y
poco rit.
a tempo
Bb7
Eb7
Ab
Fm
Bbm
Eb7
Ab
thought of you, my love. The ver-y love.
a tempo
poco rit.
l.h.

TUXEDO JUNCTION

Words: Buddy Feyne
Music: Erskine Hawkins, William Johnson & Julian Dash

Eb6
Eb7
Bb6
junc - tion where the town folks meet.
Eb7
Bb9
Eb6
Eb7
At each func - tion, in their
Bb6
Gm7
Cm7
F7
Bb
Eb9
F7
tux they greet you. Come on down, for - get your care. Come on
Bb
Eb9
F7
Bb
down, You'll find me there. So long town! I'm head -
Edim
Eb9
Bb
F7
Bb
- in' for Tux - e - do Junc - tion now.

TAKE THE 'A' TRAIN

Words & Music: Billy Strayhorn

Bbm
Eb
Cm
Eb7
Ab
To go to Sug - ar Hill 'way up in Har - lem.
Ab
Bb9(b5)
If you miss the "A" train,
Bbm
Eb
Cm
Eb7
You'll find you've missed the quick-est way to
Ab
Ab9
Db
Har - lem.
Hur - ry,
get on now it's

B♭7
com-ing
Lis - ten
to those rails a -
B♭m7
E♭9
E♭7(♭9)
A♭
thrum-ming
All
'board!
get on the
B♭9(♭5)
B♭m
E♭
Cm
E♭7
"A" train
Soon
you will be on Sug-ar Hill in
1
A♭
2
A♭
tacet
Har- lem.
Har -lem.

OH LOOK AT ME NOW

Words: John De Vries
Music: Joe Bushkin

Eb9/6 Bb9 Eb7sus4 Eb7-9 Abmaj7
I nev-er knew the tech-nique of kiss-in', I nev-er knew the
Abm6 Db7-5 Ebmaj7 Db7 C9 F9 Bb9
thrill I could get from your touch, nev-er knew much, Oh! Look At Me
Eb Eb9/6 A7-9 D7 Gm Eb7 D7
Now. I'm a new man, bet-ter than
(girl) in a whirl
3
Gm D7+5 Gm Gm7 C7 Fm
Cas-a-no-va at his best.
nev-er knew love was like this.
With a new heart,

Db7 C7 Fm Fm7 Bb7 Bb7+5
brand new start, I'm so proud I'm bust-in' my vest. So,
Gon-na be Mis-iz, not Miss.
Eb9/6 Bb9 Eb7sus4 Eb7-9 Abmaj7
I am the guy (girl) who turned out a lov-er, So, I'm the guy, (girl) who
Abm6 Db7-5 Ebmaj7 Db7
laughed at those blue dia-mond rings, one of those things,
C9 F9 Bb9 1. Eb6 Fm7 Bb9 Bb7+5 2. Eb6
Oh! Look At Me Now. Now.
3

SATIN DOLL

Words: Johnny Mercer
Music: Duke Ellington & Billy Strayhorn

Cm D7 Abm7 Db7-9 C D9 G7-9 C
Speaks Lat-in that Sat - in Doll. She's
Gm7 C7 Gm7 C7 F
no - bod-y's fool, so I'm play - ing it cool as can be, I'll
Am7 D7 Am7 D7 G7 Dm7 G7
(Spoken)
give it a whirl, but I ain't for no girl catch-ing me. Swich - E-Roo-ney
Dm7 G7 Dm7 G7 Em7 A7 Em7 A7 Cm D7
Tel - e-phone num - bers well you know, do-ing my rhum-bas with u-no, And that 'n'
Abm7 Db7-9 1. C C#dim 2. C D9 G7-9 C
my Sat - in Doll.

SWEET SUE – JUST YOU

Words: Will J. Harris
Music: Victor Young

Bm/F♯
Em7
A7
Am7/D
Cm7(7♯)
D7
lone - ly for on - ly sweet you:
know it, to show it, I'll try:
Ev - 'ry
CHORUS
Am7
D7
Am7
D7
D13(♭9)
G6
star a - bove knows the one I love Sweet Sue,
D13(♭9)
G6
Am7
D7
just you And the moon up high knows the
Am7
D7
D13(♭9)
G6
D13(♭9)
G6
rea - son why Sweet Sue, it's you

D
Dm7
G7
Dm7
G7
Bm7-5
E7
Bm7-5
E7
No-one else it seems ever shares my dreams And with-
Am
Am(#7)
Am7
Am7-5
D7
Am7
out you, dear, I don't know what I'd do, In this heart of mine
D7
Am7
D7
D13(♭9)
G6
C9
you live all the time Sweet Sue, Just
1 G
Am7
D7
tacet
2 G
C
Cm6
Gmaj7
You. Ev-'ry You.
poco rit.
8

Classical

NOCTURNE IN 'E' FLAT

By: Frederic Chopin

a tempo
fz p
cresc.
p
pp
f
poco rall.
Ped. come prima
a tempo
fz p
p

pp
poco rubato
sempre
pp
dolcissimo
p
con forza
stretto
8va
ff
senza tempo
cresc.
dim.
rall.
smorz.
a tempo
pp
ppp

MELODY IN 'F'

By: Anton Rubinstein

HUMORESQUE

By: Antonin Dvorak

(a)
(b)
rit.
f dim.
a tempo
pp
cresc.
rit.
a)
b)

a tempo
dim.
dim.

pp
rit.
a tempo
mf
f
dim.
p
p
dim.
rit.
pp dim.
ppp

BLUE DANUBE

By: Johann Strauss Jr.

2.
dolce
Fine
D.S. al Fine

3.
p
p cresc.
f
p
p
sf
p

4.

5.
p
pp
1.
2.
f
ff
1

ff
sf
sf
1
Coda
p
tr
f
cresc.
pp
tr
cresc.
f
cresc.
ff
sf

CLAIR DE LUNE

By: Claude Debussy

Tempo rubato
pp
m.d.
peu á peu cresc. et animé
8
dim. molto
un poco mosso
pp

p
p
cresc.
En animant
più cresc.

f
dim.
calmato
pp

a Tempo I°

pp
morendo jusqu'à la fin
(R.H.)
(R.H.)
(R.H.)
(R.H.)

LIEBESTRAÜME

By: Franz Liszt

poco cresc. ed agitato
cresc.
8va

Più animato, con passione
mf
cresc.
f
sempre stringendo
ff

ff
sempre più rinf
appassionato assai
8va

affrettando
8va
dim.
leggiero
ritard
Tempo primo
dolce
armonioso

poco - - - a - - - poco - - ritenuto
più smorz. e rit.

TRÄUMEREI

By: Robert Schumann

International
Songs

IN THE OLD BAZAAR IN CAIRO

Words & Music: Charlie Chester,
Ken Morris & Clinton Ford

Cm Fm Ab7 G7 Cm
Bet you'd look a smash - er in an old loin cloth In the old ba - zaar in Cai - ro
Fun - ny lit - tle odds and ends float - ing down the Nile From the old ba - zaar in Cai - ro
Bb7 Eb Bb7 Eb
You can buy most an - y - thing Thin bulls, fat cows, a lit - tle bit of string
You can buy most an - y - thing Sheeps eyes, sand pies, a watch with - out a spring
C Fm G7
You can pur - chase an - y - thing you wish, A clock a dish and some - thing for your Aun - tie Nel - lie.
You can buy a pom - e - gran - ate too A wat - er bag, a lit - tle bit of ho - key po - key
Cm Fm Cm Fm Cm
Har - em, scar - em, what d'ya think of that Bare knees, strip - tease, dan - cing on the mat
Yash - macs, pon - te - fracts, what a strange af - fair Dark girls, fair girls, some with gin - ger hair The
Cm Fm Ab7 G7 Cm Cm
Um - pa! um - pa! that's e - nough of that In the old ba - zaar in Cai - ro
rest of this is fun - ny but they cen - sor out it there In the old ba - zaar in Cai - ro

Y VIVA ESPANA

English Words: Eddie Seago
Original Lyric: Leo Rozenstraeten
Music: Leo Caerts

teach her hot blood - ed la - tin ways
But ev - en Ru - dy
G
F
would have felt the strain
of mak - ing smooth ad - van - ces in the
F
E
B7
(CHORUS)
rain
Oh this year I'm off to sun - ny Spain
La la la la la la la
E E7
A
Y(E) Vi - va Es - pa - ña
I'm
la
A
A6/C♯ Cdim
E7

tak - ing the Cos - ta Bra - va plane
la la la la la la la la
Y(E) Vi -
-va Es - pa - ña
If you'd like to chat a mat - a -
A
-dor in some cool ca - ba - ña
A6/C♯ Cdim E7
And meet se - nor - i - tas by the score
Es -

VERSE 2. Quite by chance to hot romance I found the answer
Flamenco dancers are far the finest bet
There was one who whispered "Whoo hasta la vista"
Each time I kissed him behind the castanet
He rattled his maracas close to me
In no time I was trembling at the knee.
(CHORUS)

VERSE 3. When they first arrive the girls are pink and pasty
But oh so tasty as soon as they go brown
I guess they know every fellow will be queueing
To do the wooing his girlfriend won't allow,
But still I think today's a lucky day
That's why I've learned the way to shout "ole".
(CHORUS)

TENNESSEE WALTZ

Words & Music: Redd Stewart
& Pee Wee King

C G7 C E7
friend stole my sweet-heart from me I re-mem-ber the night and the
F C G7
TEN-NES-SEE WALTZ Now I know just how much I have lost Yes I
C C7 F
lost my lit-tle dar-lin' the night they were play-ing The
C G7 1 C 2 C
beau-ti-ful TEN-NES-SEE WALTZ. I was WALTZ.

STARS FELL ON ALABAMA

Words: Mitchell Parish
Music: Frank Perkins

F G7 C A7 F G7 G+ C Gm A7
stars fell on Al-a-ba-ma last night, I can't for-get the
D7 G+ C Cdim F G7
glam-our, your eyes held a ten-der light, and stars fell on Al-a-ba-ma last
C F G7 C F G7 C Cdim F G7
night, I nev-er planned in my im-a-gi-na-tion a sit-u-a-tion so hea-ven-
C F G7 Am C B7
-ly, A fair-y land where no one else could en-ter, and in the cen-ter just you and
E G7 C Gm A7 D7 G+ C Cdim
me, dear, My heart beat like a ham-mer, my arms wound a-round you tight, and
F G7 1. C A7 F G7 2. C F G7 C
stars fell on Al-a-ba-ma last night. night.

THE SONG FROM "MOULIN ROUGE"
(Where Is Your Heart)

Words: William Engvick
Music: Georges Auric

Bb Fm7 Bb6 Bb7 Eb Fm7 Bb7
here, but WHERE IS YOUR HEART? It's a sad thing to re-al-
Ebmaj7 Eb6 Fm6 G7 Cm Cm6 D7-9
ize that you've a heart that nev-er melts. When we kiss, do you close your
Gm Cm7 F7 Bb Eb
eyes, pre-tend-ing that I'm some-one else? You must break the
Gm Cm7 F7 Fm7 Bb7 Fm
spell, this cloud that I'm un-der. So please won't you
Fm7 Edim Fm7 Bb6 Bb7 1. Eb Bb7 2. Eb Ab6 Eb
tell, dar-ling, WHERE IS YOUR HEART? When HEART?
dim. e rall.

ARRIVEDERCI ROMA

Music: Renato Rascel
Words: Garinei & Giovannini
English lyric: Carl Sigman

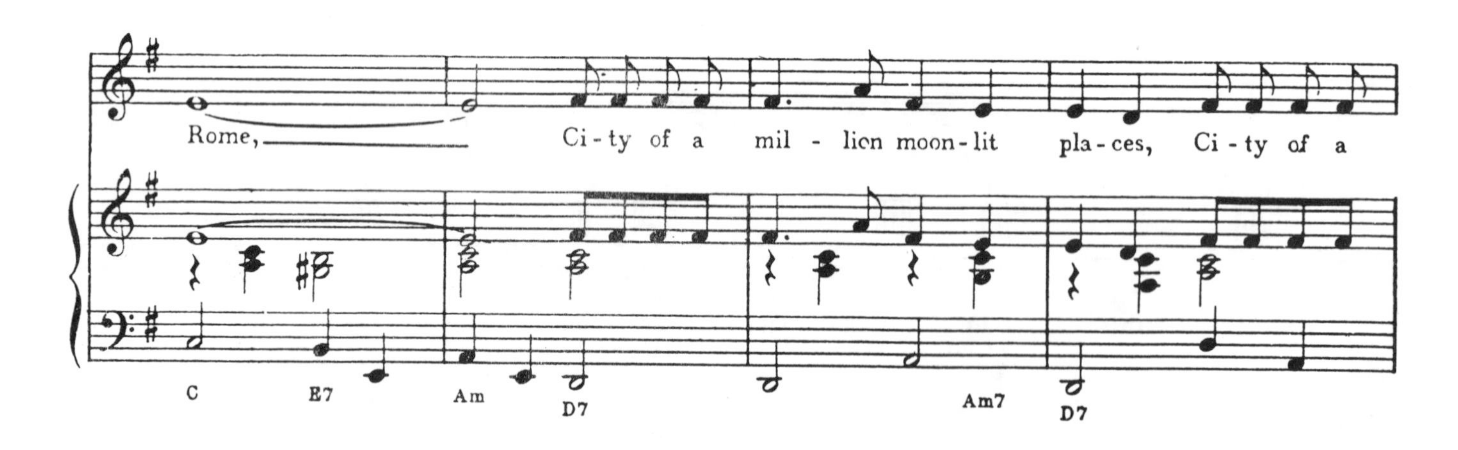

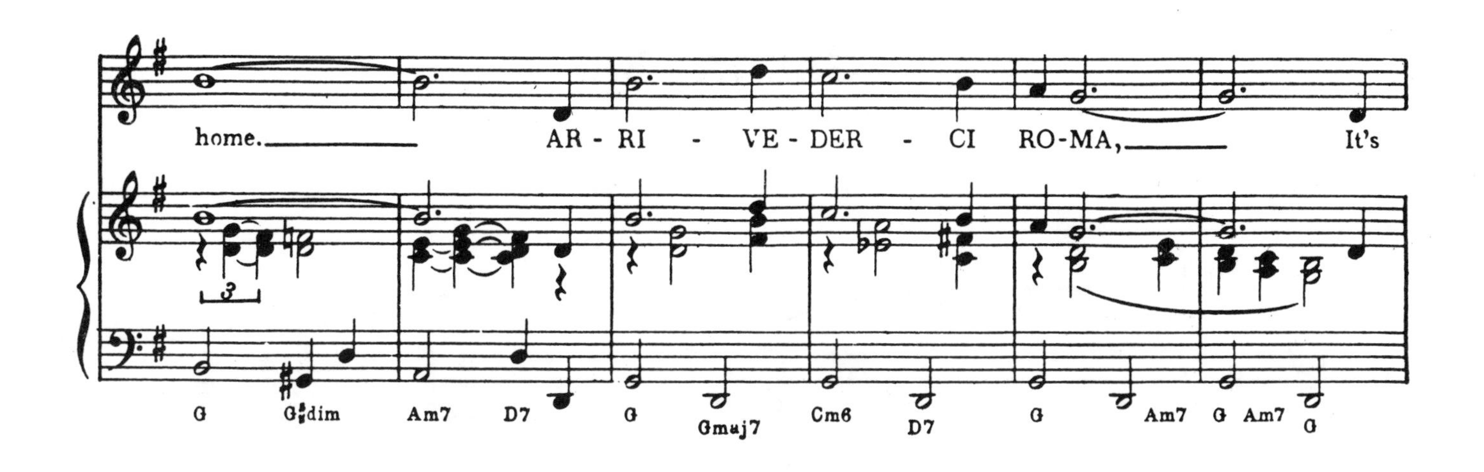
home. ARRI - VE - DER - CI RO - MA, It's
G G#dim Am7 D7 G Gmaj7 Cm6 D7 G Am7 G Am7 G

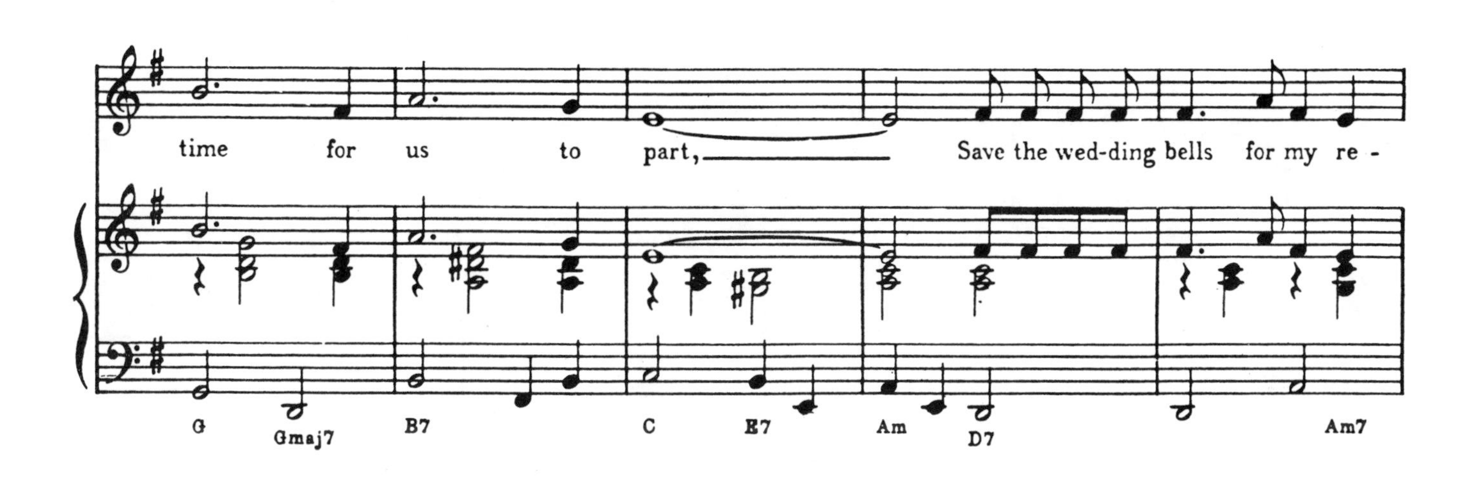
time for us to part, Save the wed-ding bells for my re -
G Gmaj7 B7 C E7 Am D7 Am7

-turn - ing, Keep my lov-er's arms out-stretched and yearn-ing, Please be sure the flame of love keeps
D7 Am7 D7 Am7

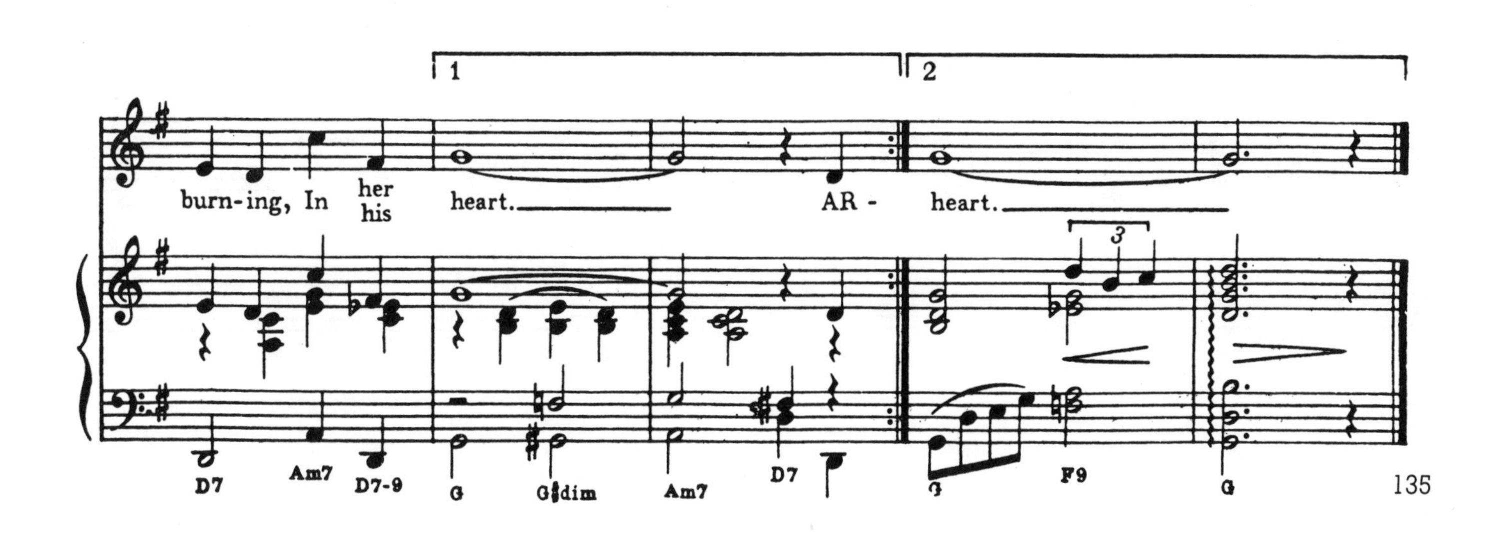
1
2
burn-ing, In her his heart. AR - heart.
D7 Am7 D7-9 G G#dim Am7 D7 G F9 G

GALWAY BAY

Words & Music: Dr Arthur Colahan

C7
F
Cm6
D7
ten.
trout stream, The wo-men in the meadows making hay, And to sit be-side a turf fire in the
their way, They scorn'd us just for be-ing what we are, But they might as well go chas-ing af-ter
G7
C7
F
F
cab - in, And watch the bare-foot Gos-soons at their play. For the
moon-beams, Or light a pen-ny can-dle from a star. And if
there is going to be a life here-af-ter, And some-how I am sure there's going to be, I will
ask my God to let me make my hea-ven, In that dear land a-cross the I-rish sea.
rit.

DO YOU KNOW THE WAY TO SAN JOSE

Words: Hal David
Music: Burt Bacharach

B♭6
F
C7(sus)
way to San_ Jo - se? I'm go - ing back to find some_ peace of
raised in San_ Jo - se. I'm go - ing back to find some_ peace of
C7
Am7
Dm7
mind in San_ Jo - se. L. A. is a great_ big free - way.
mind in San_ Jo - se. Fame and for-tune is_ a mag - net.
mf
Am7
Dm7
Am
Put a hun-dred down_ and buy_ a car._
It can pull you far_ a - way_ from home._
F♯m7-5
Gm7/F
C/E
In a week may - be two, they'll make you a star.
With a dream in your heart you're nev - er a - lone.

Gm7
C
(Tacet)
Weeks turn in - to years. How quick they pass, and all the stars
Dreams turn in - to dust and blow a - way, and there you are
that nev - er were are park-ing cars and pump - ing gas.
with-out a friend. You pack your car and ride a - way.
mp
1.
2.
F
I've got lots of
mp
sfz sfz sfz
sfz sfz sfz
B♭6
Fmaj7
friends in San Jo - se.
mf
mp

F
B♭ 6
Fmaj7
Do you know the way to San_ Jo - se?
mf
Can't wait to get back to San_ Jo - se.
mp
mf
mp
(Tacet)
dim.
poco
8va bassa
a
poco
Keep repeating and fade

BRAZIL

Music: Ary Barroso
English lyric: S. K. Russell

your heart in it, And so I
G G+ G6 Gmaj7(5♯) Am Fmaj7 Am6 F♯dim
dream of old Bra-
G G+ G6 Gmaj7(5♯) Am Fmaj7 Am6 F♯dim
CHORUS
zil Where hearts were en-ter-tain-ing June,
G G+ G6 G+ G G+ G6 G+ Am F
We stood be-neath an am-ber moon
Am6 F Am F Am6 F Am F Am6 F

And soft - ly mur - mur'd "Some - day soon" We kissed
Am F Am6 Cm6 G G+ G6 Gmaj7(5#) Am Fmaj7
and cling to - ge - ther, Then to - mor - row
Am6 F#dim G G7 Gb7 F7 E7 Dm E7
was an - oth - er day The morn - ing found me miles a - way
Dm E7
with still a mil - lion things to say
Dm E7 Am F Am6

Now When twi - light dims the sky a - bove,
F Am F Am Cm F♯dim G
Re - call - ing thrills of our love, There's one thing
D7 G C♯dim Am7 E♭9
I'm cer-tain of; Re - turn I will to
D7 D11 G G+ G6 Gmaj7(5♯) Am Fmaj7 Am6 F♯dim G G+ G6 Gmaj7(5♯)
1 2
old Bra - zil. Bra -
L.H.
Am Fmaj7 Am6 F♯dim G G+ G6 G+ Am F Am6 F♯dim G G+ G6

GRANADA

Music: Agustin Lara
English lyric: Dorothy Dodd

Beguine
Chorus
C
C6
Em
C
Em7
C°
The dawn in the sky greets the day with a sigh for GRA-
And when day is done and the sun starts to set in GRA-
mp-mf
Dm7 G7
Dm G7
G7
NA-DA.
For she can re-
NA-DA.
I en-vy the
G7
D7 G7
C
C6
mem-ber the splen-dour that once was GRA-NA-DA.
blush of the snow-clad Si-er-ra Ne-va-da.
Dm C
C6
Em
It still can be found in the hills all a-
mp-mf

C Em
round as I wan-der a- long, En-
B7 B7+ B7 C Em C Em
tranc'd by the beau-ty be - fore me,- En - tranced by a
B7 B7+ Em D#7 C#o G7
land full of sun-shine and flow - ers and song. And
D. S. al
Dm C C C7 F
For soon it will wel - come the stars while a

Fm
C
Fm6
C
thou-sand gui - tars play a soft hab - an - er - a;
Then
Fm
C
C°
moon-lit GRA - NA - DA will live a-gain the glo-ry of
G7
G9+
1. C
C°
G7
yes-ter-day, ro - man-tic and gay.
C
C°
G7
2. C
Fm
C
Fm
C
G9+
C
The gay.
p

I LEFT MY HEART IN SAN FRANCISCO

Words: Douglas Cross
Music: George Cory

Slow, steady beat
CHORUS
Bbmaj9
Gm7
C#dim
Cm7
heart in San Fran-cis-co.
High on a hill,
Eb
F7
F+
Bbmaj7
it calls to me.
To be where lit-tle ca-ble cars
Dm7
Bbm6
Am
Am7
D7-9
climb half-way to the stars!
The morn-ing fog
cresc.
C9
C7-5
F9
Bdim
may chill the air I don't care! My love waits there in San Fran-
dim.

Cm7
F9
Eb6
F9
Ebmaj9
Eb6
D
C
cis-co,
A - bove the blue
and wind - y
sea.
cresc.
D7
D9
D7-9
D9
G7+
G9
F
G7
C9
Gm7
When I come home to you, San Fran - cis - co,
f
C9
Bmaj9
C9
Cm7
F7-5
1.
Bb6
Abmaj9
your gold - en sun will shine for me!
dim.
Bbmaj9
Bbmaj7
Cm7
C#dim
2.
Bb6
Abmaj9
Bbmaj9
Gbmaj7
Bbmaj9
I left my
me!
mp
dim. e rit.
mp

Rock
'n'
Roll

LONG TALL SALLY

Words & Music: Enotris Johnson, Richard Penniman & Robert Blackwell

1.2.
3. (last time)
Hav-in' me some fun to - night. yeah! 2. Well, 3. Well, I yeah! We're gon-na
have some fun to - night, Gon-na have some fun to - night woo! We're gon-na
have some fun to-night, Ev - 'ry-thing will be all right. We're gon-na
have some fun, gon- na have some fun to-night!
Bb9
F
Bb9
F
C7
Bb9
F
Gm7
F

ROCK AROUND THE CLOCK

Words & Music: Max C. Freedman
& Jimmy de Knight

CHORUS
1. Put your glad rags on and join me, hon, We'll have some fun when the
(2. When the) clock strikes two, and three and four, If the band slows down we'll
(3. When the) chimes ring five and six and seven, We'll be rock - in' up in
(4. When it's) eight, nine, ten, e - lev - en, too, I'll be go - in' strong and
(5. when the) clock strikes twelve, we'll cool off, then, Start a rock - in' 'round the
F C♯dim F C♯dim F
clock strikes one, We're gon-na rock a - round the clock to - night, We're gon-na
yell for more, We're gon-na rock a - round the clock to - night, We're gon-na
sev - enth heav'n We're gon-na rock a - round the clock to - night, We're gon-na
so will you, We're gon-na rock a - round the clock to - night, We're gon-na
clock a - gain, We're gon-na rock a - round the clock to - night, We're gon-na
F7 B♭9
rock, rock, rock, 'til broad day - light, We're gon-na rock, gon-na rock a - round the clock to - night.
F B♭6 F B♭6 F G7 Gm7 C7+5 Gm7 F
1-4
5
2. When the
3. When the
4. When it's
5. When the
F F

THIS OLE HOUSE

Words & Music: Stuart Hamblen

CHORUS
Ab
Eb
Bb7
Ain't a-gon-na need this house no long-er: ain't a-gon-na need this house no more. Ain't got time to fix the shing-les: ain't got time to fix the floor. Ain't got time to oil the hing-es nor to mend no win-dow panes. Ain't gon-na need this house no long-er; He's a-get-tin' rea-dy to meet his fate. This old fate.
1-2 To Verse
3

BLUE SUEDE SHOES

Words & Music: Carl Lee Perkins

Knock me down, step in my face, slan-der my name all o-ver the place;
Burn my house, steal my car, drink my li-quor from my old fruit jar;
Tacet
F
Do an-y-thing that you want to do, but uh-uh, hon-ey lay off of my shoes
Don't you step on my Blue Suede Shoes.
You can do an-y-thing but lay
Bb
C7
off of my blue suede shoes.
shoes.
C7sus4
Bb7
1
2
3

JAILHOUSE ROCK

Words & Music: Jerry Leiber
& Mike Stoller

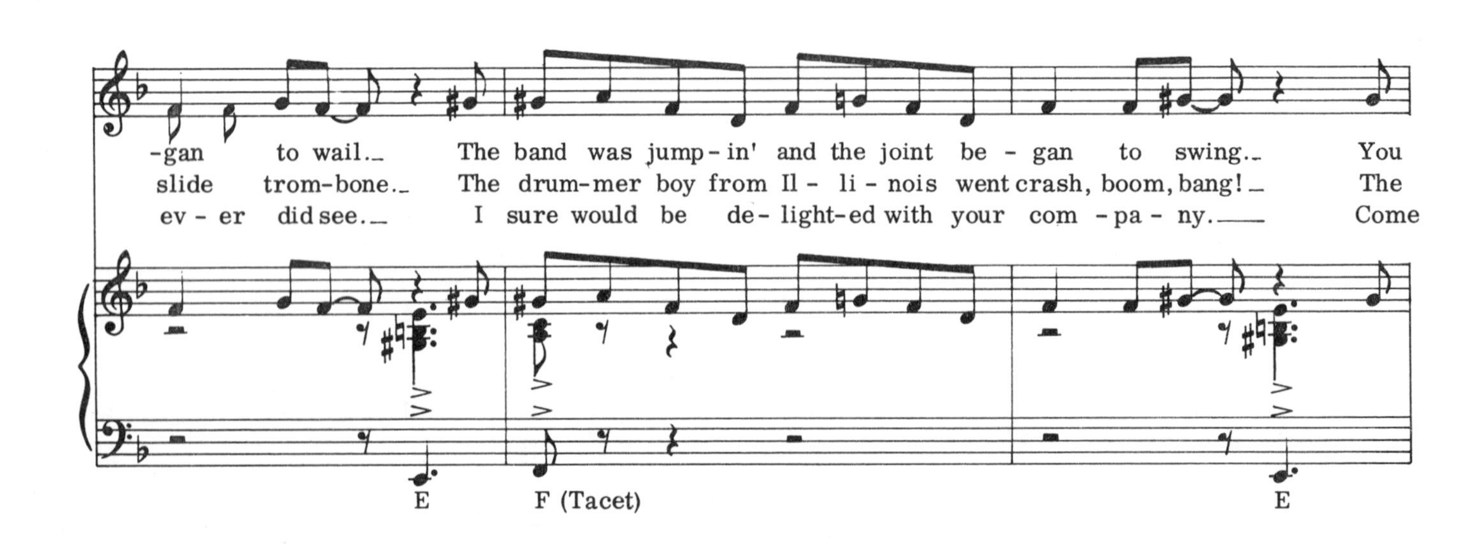

EXTRA CHORUSES

4. The sad sack was a-sittin' on a block of stone,
Way over in the corner weeping all alone.
The warden said, "Hey buddy, don't you be no square,
If you can't find a partner, use a wooden chair!"
Let's rock, etc.

5. Shifty Henry said to Bugs, "For Heaven's sake,
No one's lookin', now's our chance to make a break."
Bugsy turned to Shifty and he said, "Nix, nix,
I wanna stick around a while and get my kicks,"
Let's rock, etc.

TELSTAR

By: Joe Meek

2
Cm7
F7
B♭
Gm
Cm
F7
B♭
Gm
Cm
F7
B♭
Gm
Cm
F7
B♭
Gm
Cm
F7
B♭
Gm

Cm7
F7
B♭
Gm7
E♭
F7
B♭/D
Gm
E♭
F7
B♭
Gm
Cm
F7
B♭

CHANTILLY LACE

Words & Music: J. P. Richardson

big eyed girl — to make me act so fun – ny, spend my dog – gone mon–ey, I
G
To Coda
feel real loose like a long – necked goose, like a (spoken) Wa, ba–by that's what I like! —
D7
G tacet
VERSES
(Spoken) (1) Huh?
Will I what?
(2) Huh?
ha ha ha
Huh? What's that?
Pick
D7
G
Do I what?
Will I what?
you up at eight?
And don't be late?
You gotta be jokin' woman,
D7
G
G7

VERSE 3 (patter) Woo ha ha ha ha ha honey, you're tearin' me up on this telephone.
I swear I don't know what I'm gonna do with you, you yap and yap
and yap and yap and yap but when you break it all down you know
what I like. (to CHORUS)

GOOD GOLLY MISS MOLLY

Words & Music: Robert Blackwell
& John Marascalco

Well from the ear-ly, ear-ly morn-in' To the ear-ly, ear-ly night, When I
C7+
F
Bb7
F
Bb7
caught Miss Mol-ly rock-in' at the House of Blue Lights,_Ooh Good Gol-ly Miss
F
Mol-ly, Yeah you sure_like a ball._ When you're rock-in' and a
Bb7
F
roll-in' Can't you hear_your Mom-ma call? Well now
C7
Bb7
F
C7+

Mom - ma, Pop - pa told me "Son you'd bet - ter watch your step" What I
F Bb7 F Bb7
knew a - bout Miss Mol - ly, Got - ta watch my dad-dy my-self. Good Gol - ly Miss
Mol - ly Yeah you sure like a ball When you're shak - in' and a
Bb7 F
shout - in' Can't you hear your Mom-ma call?
C7 Bb7 F Eb F

ALL SHOOK UP

Words & Music: Otis Blackwell &Elvis Presley

hands are sha - ky and my knees are weak, I can't seem to stand on my
Bb
own two feet, Who do you thank when you have such luck? I'm in love! I'm
All shook up! Mm mm, oh, oh, yeah, yeah!
Eb7 F7 Bb Eb7 Bb
1. Please don't ask what's on my mind, I'm a lit - tle mixed up but I'm feel - in' fine When I'm
2. Tongue get's tied when I try to speak, My in - side shakes like a leaf on a tree, There's
Eb7 Bb
Opt.
near that girl that I love best, My heart beats so it scares me to death!
on-ly one cure for this soul of mine, That's to have the girl that I love so fine! She
Eb7 F7

touched my hand, What a chill I got,_ Her kiss - es are like_ a vol -
B♭
ca - no that's hot!_ I'm proud to say she's my but - ter cup,_ I'm in love! I'm
1
All shook up!_ Mm mm oh, oh, yeah,_ yeah!_ 2. My
E♭7 F7 B♭ E♭7 B♭
2
yeah! I'm All shook up!_ Mm mm oh, oh, yeah,_ yeah! I'm
B♭ E♭7 F7 B♭
All! shook up!_ Mm mm oh, oh, yeah,_ yeah! I'm all shook up!_
E♭7 F7 B♭

GET BACK

Words & Music: John Lennon & Paul McCartney

B♭
F
F7
to where you once be-longed.
Get back!
Get back!
Get back
B♭
F
to where you once be-longed.
(Get back, Jo Jo)
Sweet Lor-et-ta Mod-ern thought she was a wo-man, but
B♭
F
she was an-oth-er man.
All the girls a-round her say she's got it com-ing,
But,
B♭
F
F7
F7
she gets it while she can.
Get back!
Get back!
Get back

B♭
F
F7
to where you once be - longed. Get back! Get back! Get back
B♭
B♭7
to where you once be - longed.
F
B♭
F
F7
B♭
(Spoken:) Get back, Loretta. Your mother is waiting for you.
D. S. and fade out on Chorus
F
B♭
F
F7
Wearin' her high heel shoes and her low neck sweater, Get back home, Loretta. Get back!

SINGIN' IN THE RAIN

Words: Arthur Freed
Music: Nacio Herb Brown

G
dark up a - bove, The sun's in my heart And I'm rea dy for
love. Let the storm y clouds chase Ev -'ry - one from the place, Come
Ddim
D7
on with the rain, I've a smile on my face. I'll walk down the lane With a
G
Fine
hap- py re - frain, And sing - in' just Sing - in' In The Rain.
Fine

Eb7
G
Eb7
Why am I smil-in' and why do I sing? Why does De-cem-ber seem
mp
G
D7
G
sun-ny as Spring? Why do I get up each morn-ing to start
E7
A7
Bb7
Hap-py and het up with joy in my heart? Why is each new task a
Eb
F7
Eb7
D7
D.S. al Fine
tri-fle to do? Be-cause I am liv-ing a life full of you I'm
D.S. al Fine

THE WINDMILLS OF YOUR MIND

Words: Alan & Marilyn Bergman
Music: Michel Legrand

Gmaj7
Cmaj7
F♯m7-5
moon.
stream.
Like a clock whose hands are sweep-ing past the min-utes of its face, And the world is like an
B7
A♯dim
B7
ap-ple whirl-ing si-lent-ly in space, Like the cir-cles that you find in The Wind-mills Of Your
Em
Am7
Mind! Keys that jin-gle in your pock-et, words that jan-gle in your head, Why did sum-mer go so
D7
Gmaj7
G7
quick-ly? Was it some-thing that you said? Lov-ers walk a-long a shore and leave their foot-prints in the
Cmaj 7
F♯7
Bm
sand. Is the sound of dis-tant drum-ming just the fin-gers of your hand? Pic-tures hang-ing in a

E7
Am
D7
hall-way and the frag-ment of a song, Half re-mem-bered names and fac-es, but to whom do they be-
Gmaj7
Cmaj7
F♯m7-5
long? When you knew that it was o-ver you were sud-den-ly a-ware That the au-tumn leaves were
(Girl) When you knew that it was o-ver in the au-tumn of good-byes, For a mo-ment you could
poco a poco ritard.
B7
Em
turn-ing to the col-or of her hair!
not re-call the col-or of his eyes!
Like a cir-cle in a spi-ral, like a wheel with-in a
a tempo
B7
A♯dim
wheel, Nev-er end-ing or be-gin-ning on an ev-er spin-ning reel, As the im-a-ges un-
Em
B7
Em
wind, Like the cir-cles that you find in The Wind-mills Of Your Mind!
poco a poco ritard.

RAINDROPS KEEP FALLING ON MY HEAD

Words: Hal David
Music: Burt Bacharach

B♭/C
C
F
head. They keep fall-in' so I just did me some talk-in' to the
Fmaj7
F7
B♭
sun. And I said I did-n't like the way he got things
Am7
D7
D9
Am7
D7
Gm7
done. Sleep-in' on the job. Those rain-drops are fall-in' on my
B♭/C
C
F
head. They keep fall-in'! But there's one thing I know

Fmaj7
B7
B♭
C
C7
The blues they send to meet me won't de - feat
Am7
D9
me. It won't be long till hap - pi - ness steps up
Gm7
Gm9
Gm7
B♭/C
C
B♭/C
C
to greet me.
mf
F
Fmaj7
F7
Rain - drops keep fall - in' on my head, but that does-n't mean my eyes will
mp

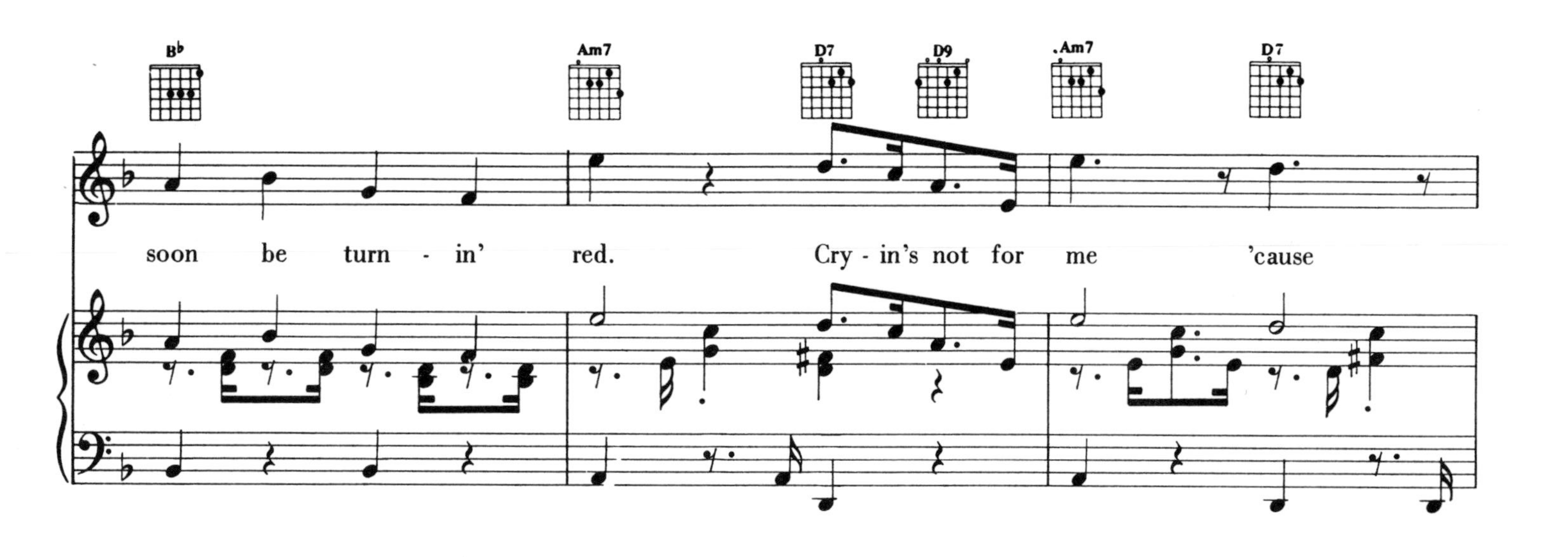
B♭
Am7
D7
D9
Am7
D7
soon be turn - in' red. Cry - in's not for me 'cause

Gm7
B♭/C
C
I'm nev - er gon - na stop the rain by com-plain-in'. Be - cause I'm

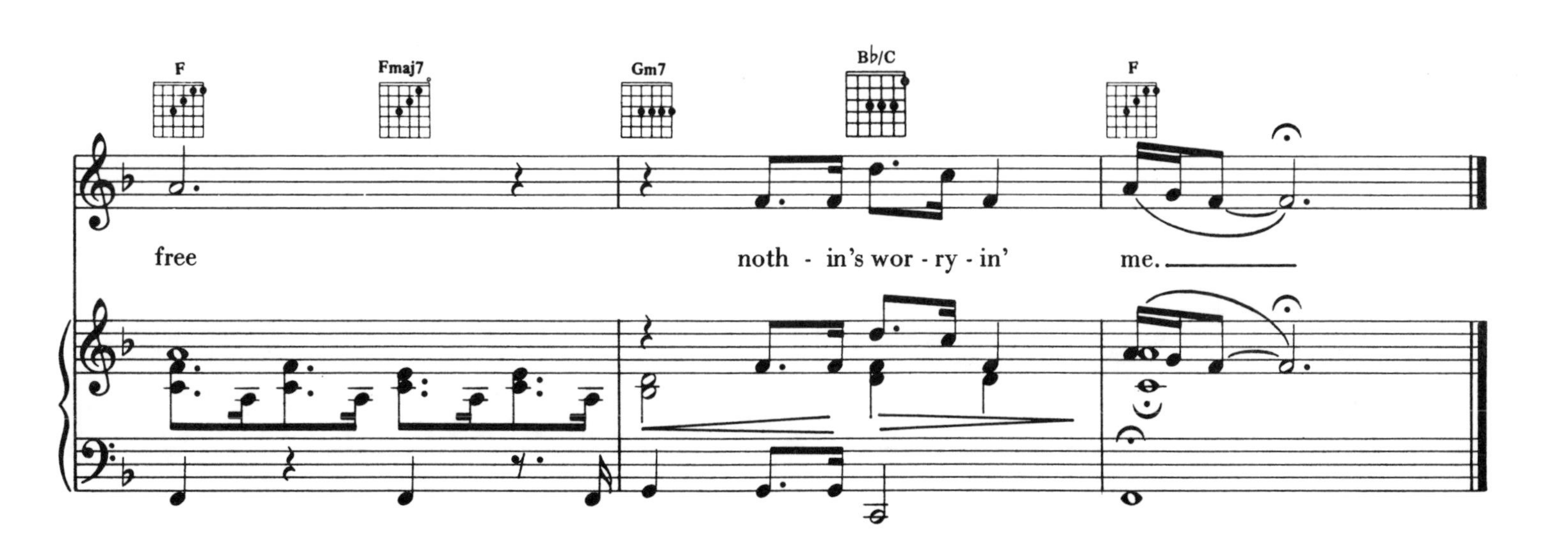
F
Fmaj7
Gm7
B♭/C
F
free noth - in's wor - ry - in' me.

FROM RUSSIA WITH LOVE

Words & Music: Lionel Bart

mo-ment, But oh, you haun ted me so. Still my tongue tied
Am7 D7 G Gmaj7 G6 Am7
young pride, Would not let my love for you show In case you'd say no
D7 G B7 Em Am6 B7 F#7
To Rus-sia I flew but there and then, I sud-den-ly
B7 Em F#7 B7 Em
knew you'd care a-gain My run-ning a-round is through, I
Em7 Em6 Am6 B7 E7 Am
fly to you from Rus-sia with love. From love.
Em B7 B7 Em Em

MRS ROBINSON

Words & Music: Paul Simon

B♭
Gm
B♭
God bless you, please, Mrs. Rob - in - son,
Heav-en holds a place
Gm
E♭
Cm
for those who pray,
(Hey, hey, hey,
G
hey, hey, hey.
)
G7
Verse:
1. We'd like to know a lit - tle bit a - bout you for our files,

C7
We'd like to help you learn to help your-
C9
F7
B♭
self.
Look a-round you, all you see are
E♭
Cm
G
sym-pa-thet-ic eyes,
Stroll a-round
F7
the grounds un-til you feel at home.
And here's to you
D.S. al Coda

Coda
G
Verse:
G7
2. Hide it in a hid - ing place where
3. Sit - ting on a so - fa on a
no one ev - er goes,
Sun - day af - ter - noon,
C7
Put it in your pan - try with your cup - cakes,
Go - ing to the can - di - dates' de - bate,
F7
B♭
It's a lit - tle se - cret, just the Rob -
Laugh a - bout it, shout a - bout it,

E♭
Cm
G
- in - son's af - fair,
Most of all,
When you've got to choose,
Ev - 'ry way you look
F7
you've got to hide it from the kids. Coo, coo, ca - choo,
at it, you lose. Where have you gone,
Chorus:
B♭
Gm
B♭
Mrs. Rob - in - son, Je - sus loves you more
Joe Di - mag - gi - o? A na - tion turns its
Gm
E♭
F7
than you will know, (Wo, wo, wo.)
lone - ly eyes to you, (Woo, woo, woo.)

B♭
Gm
God bless you, please, Mrs. Rob - in - son,
What's that you say, Mrs. Rob - in - son,
B♭
Gm
E♭
Heav - en holds a place for those who pray.
"Jolt - in' Joe" has left and gone a - way.
Cm
G
(Hey, hey, hey, hey, hey, hey.
(Hey, hey, hey, hey, hey, hey.
)
)
1.
2. G7add6

LOVE IS A SONG

Words: Larry Morey
Music: Frank Churchill

Am7 D7 Bm F♯ Am6 G D7 G Am7 Bm D7 G B7 Em Em7
fleet - ing, Hope may die, yet love's beau - ti - ful mu - sic, Comes each
A9 F♯m A7 Am7 Cm6 F♯dim D7 G B7 Em Bm F♯ Am7 D7 Bm D7
day like the dawn. Love is a song that nev - er ends;
G B7 Em Bm F♯ Am7 D7 Bm F♯ Am6 G D7 G Am7 Bm D7
One sim-ple theme re - peat - ing, Like the voice of a heav - en - ly
1 2
G B7 Em Em7 Am7 D7 G Em Am D+ D7 G E♭- G6
choir love's sweet mu-sic flows on. on.
rall e dim

LOVE'S ROUNDABOUT
(La Ronde De L'Amour)

French Words: Louis Ducreux
English Words: Harold Purcell
Music: Oscar Straus

A7 D A7 D A
Round we must go, year in, year out. Tin - ker,
When you are on love's round - a - bout. Bank - er,
S'en vont par un mê - me che - min. Hon - nête
Et le nu - a - ge tombe en pluie! Tour - ne,
E7 A E7 A
Tail - or, Sol - dier or Sail - or Dream as the world goes
Ba - ker, Can - dle - stick ma - ker. This is the call we
hom - me, ca - nail - le ten - dre, A - ris - to - crate ou
tour - ne le ciel en fê - te! Tour - nent le lune et
E A E7
rid - ing by, Turn the pa - ges back thro' the
all o - bey. When love starts its round - a - bout
bien sol - dat, Quand l'a - mour vient vous sur -
le so - leil! Tour - ne, tour - ne, vieil - le pla -
A E7 A E7 A7
a - ges; What are their names? Just you and I.
twirl - ing Off we go whirl - ing on our way.
pren - dre. En - tres en danse d'un mê - me pas!
nè - te! Tour - nent la vie et l'arc - en - ciel!

D A7 Em A7
You're the one I want to be nea - est, Nev - er to
From now on, we'll nev - er be part - ed, This time it's
Tour - nent, tour - nent, mes per - son - na - ges, Quand le bon -
Cœur bri - sé, quand pas - se la Ro - de Tour - ne la
D Bm/G♯ A D A7
lose or be with - out. Side by side, my dar - ling, my
— love be - yond a doubt. Hold me close, the mu - sic has
heur est de re - tour. Jeune ou vieux, qu'im - por te notre
pa - ge, c'est ton tour! El - le tour - ne pour tout le
8
C♯7 D A7 D To Coda A7 D D7
dear - est Gai - ly we ride love's round - a - bout.
start - ed; Here we go round love's
â - ge! Dan - sons la ron - de de l'a - mour.
mon - de Voi - ci la ron - de
VERSE G D7 C/D D G D7 G7
Thro' the years we'll hear this mu - sic, Mak - ing each
Vers le ciel douce et lé - gè - re La ron - de
p

C
Am7
D7
G
A/B♭
D7
note float on the blue; While the fair - ground
mon - te en tour - noy - ant. El - le quit - te
C/D
D
C/G
G
Dm/G
G7
Cmaj7
C
A9
A13
tune is ring - ing, Back the thrill will still come
no - tre ter - re, No - tre ter - re noire et
D9
D/C
G/B
C
D
A7
D7
G
G6
A7
D.𝄋. al Coda
wing - ing, You will have me, And I shall have you.
clai - re Qui tourne et dan - se d'un même é - lan.
CODA
A7
D
Em7
Bm
G6
D
A7
D
round - a - bout.
de l'a - mour!
accel.
ff

MEMORIES ARE MADE OF THIS

Words & Music: Terry Gilkyson,
Richard Dehr & Frank Miller

D7 G D7 G D7 G
light-ly with a dream. Your lips and mine, Two sips of wine,
gen-rous-ly with love. One man, one wife, One love thro' life,
G D7 G D7 To Coda C Ddim C G
Mem - o - ries are made of this. Then add the wedding bells, One house where
Mem - o - ries are made of this.
G Cdim G D7 G Gmaj7 G7 C
lov-ers dwell, Three lit-tle kids For the fla-vour, Stir care-f'lly
C Ddim C G Cdim G A7 D7
thro' the days See how the fla-vour stays. These are the dreams you will sav - our.
Coda G D7 G Gdim Am7 D7 G
Mem - o - ries are made of this.

TIME ON MY HANDS

Words: Harold Adamson & Mack Gordon
Music: Vincent Youmans

Dm6
E
Fm6
A
E#
F#
A7
Dm
G7
an-swer a bove. To bring me con-so-la-tion,
slower
C
Am7
Dm7
G7
C
C+
You're my in-spir-a-tion, This is my im-ag-i-na-tion.
rit.
Refrain (Slow but with definite rhythm)
F
Fmaj7
E7
Time on my hands, You in my arms,
p-mf
Gm7
Bbm6
Noth-ing but love in

C7
Cm9
C7
F
Fmaj7
view;
Then if you fall,
E7
Gm7
Once and for all,
I'll see my dreams
Bb7
A7
F#m
F+
A
D7
come true.
Mo-ments to spare
G9
F
G9
Gm7
C7
for some one you care for;

F
Dm7
G7
C9
C#m
C9
ad lib.
One love af - fair for two. With
rit
rit L.H.
F
Fmaj7
F
D7
a tempo
time on my hands And you in my arms
a tempo
Dm7
G7
Gm7
C7
rall. e dim
And love in my heart all for
rall. e dim
1
F
Dm7
G7
C7
2
F
Db7
Bbm
F
you. you.
cresc.
a tempo
allargando

ZORBA THE GREEK
(or ZORBA'S DANCE)

Music: Mikis Theodorakis

Am.
G
Am.
D7
G
Plus vite
G
G7

C
G
3
3
Am.
3
G
3
Am.
D7
3
G
3
3
Am.
3

Vif et brillant
G
D7
sfz

HIGH NOON

Words: Ned Washington
Music: Dimitri Tiomkin

know I must be brave ___ And I must face a man who hates me ___
E♭7 A♭ C7 Fm E♭o E♭ E♭7
Or lie a cow-ard A cra-ven cow-ard Or lie a cow-ard in my grave! ___
A♭ E♭ A♭ E♭ A♭ E♭ Fm7 B♭7 E♭
Oh, to be torn 'twixt love and du-ty 'Spos-in' I lose my fair-haired beau-ty, Look at that big hand
A♭ E♭ A♭
move a-long Near-in' High Noon He made a vow while in State's pris-on Vowed it would be my
E♭ A♭ E♭
life on his-'n, I'm not a-fraid of death but, oh What will I do if you leave me?
A♭m E♭ B♭o Fm B♭7 B♭+

Do not for-sake me, oh my dar-lin'
You made that prom-ise as a bride
Eb
Eb7
Ab
Do not for-sake me, oh my dar-lin'
Al-though you're griev-in'
C7
Fm
Ebo
Ab
Eb
Ab
Eb
1
Don't think of leav-in'
Now that I need you by my side!
Ab
Eb
Ab
Eb
Fm7
Bb7
Eb
Fm7
2
side!
Wait a-long
Wait a-long
Wait a-long
Eb
Ab
Eb
Ab
Wait a-long!
8va
dim.
rall.
pp
Eb

mus-ic

KILLING ME SOFTLY WITH HIS SONG

Words: Norman Gimbel
Music: Charles Fox

I heard he sang a good song I heard he had a style
I felt all flushed with fe-ver em- bar-rassed by the crowd
He sang as if he knew me in all my dark des-pair
Bbm7
Eb
Ab
Db
And so I came to see him and list-en for a while
I felt he found my let-ters and read each one out loud
And then he looked right through me as if I was-n't there
Bbm7
Eb
Fm
C7sus4 Fm
And there he was this young boy a stran-ger to my eyes
I prayed that he would fin-ish but he just kept right on
But he was there this strang-er sing-ing clear and strong
Bbm7
Eb7
Ab
C7
Strumming my pain with his fin-gers sing-ing my life with his words
Fm
Bbm
Eb7

Kill-ing me soft - ly with his song kill-ing me soft - ly with his song tell-ing my whole
Fm
Bb
Eb
Db
To Coda
life with his words Kill - ing me soft - ly with his song
Ab
Db
Gb
1-2
3
He was strum-ming there yea he was sing -
F
Fm
Bbm
D. S. al Coda
CODA
ing my life Kill - ing me soft - ly with his
Eb
Ab
Fm
F

STREETS OF LONDON

Words & Music: Ralph McTell

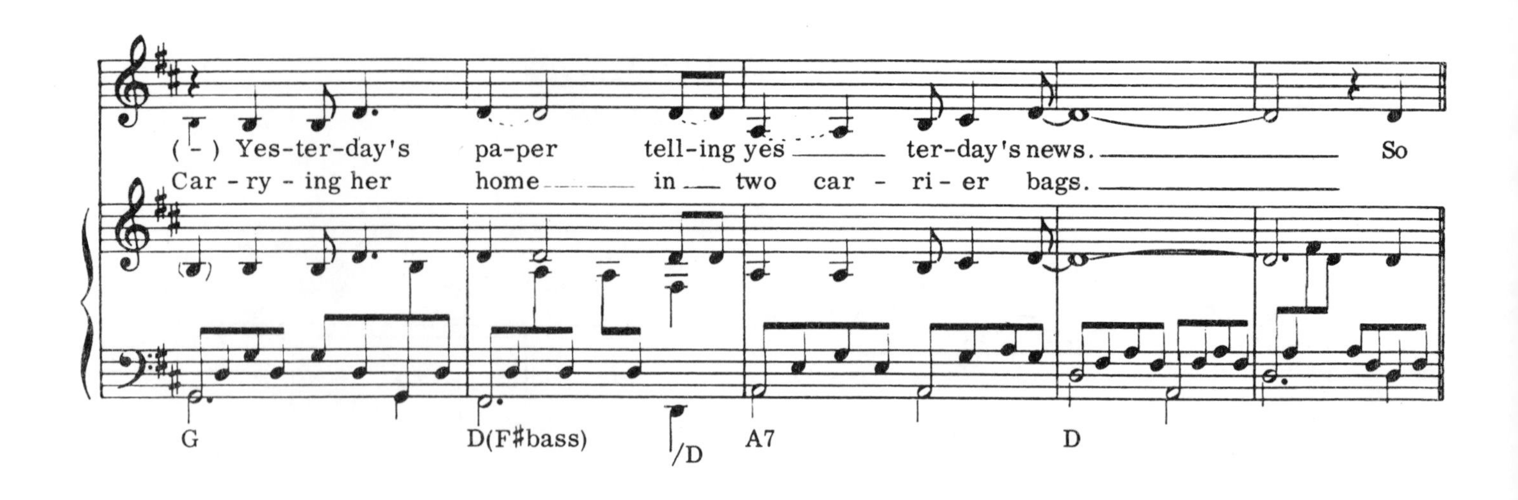
(-) Yes-ter-day's pa-per tell-ing yes ter-day's news. So
Car - ry - ing her home in two car - ri - er bags.
G
D(F#bass)
/D
A7
D

CHORUS
hcw can you tell me you're lone ly And say for you.
G
D
D/F#
A7
Bm
Bm7/A
E7/G#

that the sun don't shine? Let me take you by the hand and
A7
D
A(C#bass)

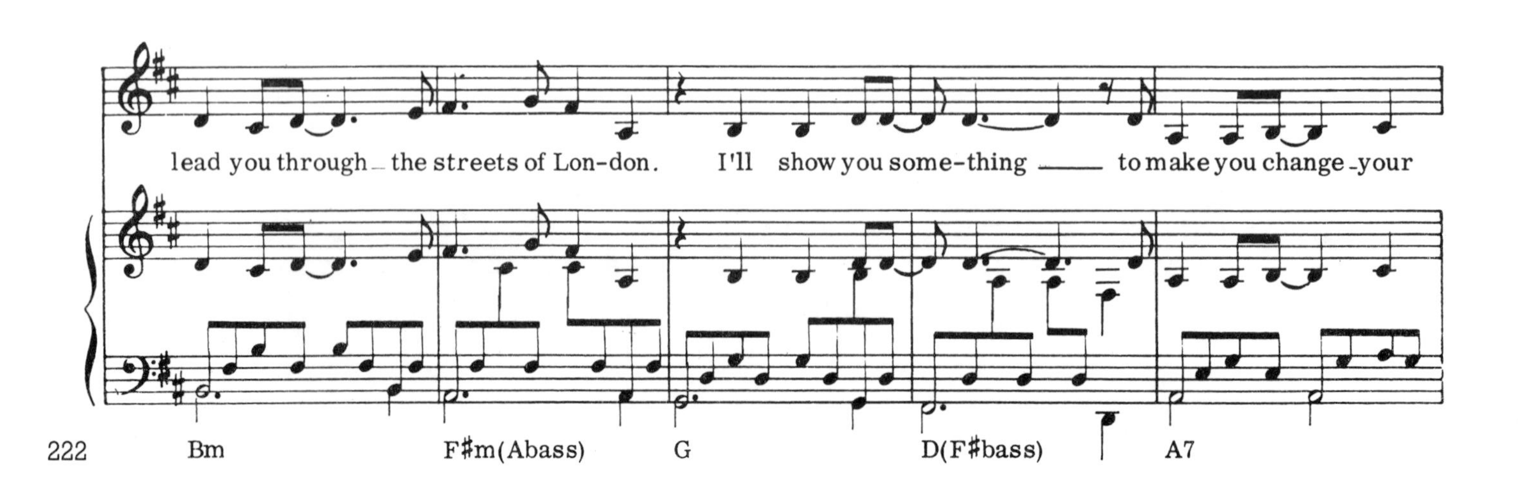
lead you through the streets of Lon-don. I'll show you some-thing to make you change your
Bm
F#m(Abass)
G
D(F#bass)
A7

1
mind.
D
A/C#
Bm
A7(sus)
A7
2
mind.
D
A(C#bass)
Bm
F#m(Abass)
G
Em/G E9/G#
A7(sus 4)
A7
2. In the all night ca-fé at a quart-er past e - lev-en
3. Have you seen the old man out - side the sea - man's miss-ion,
D
A(C#bass)
Bm
F#m(Abass)

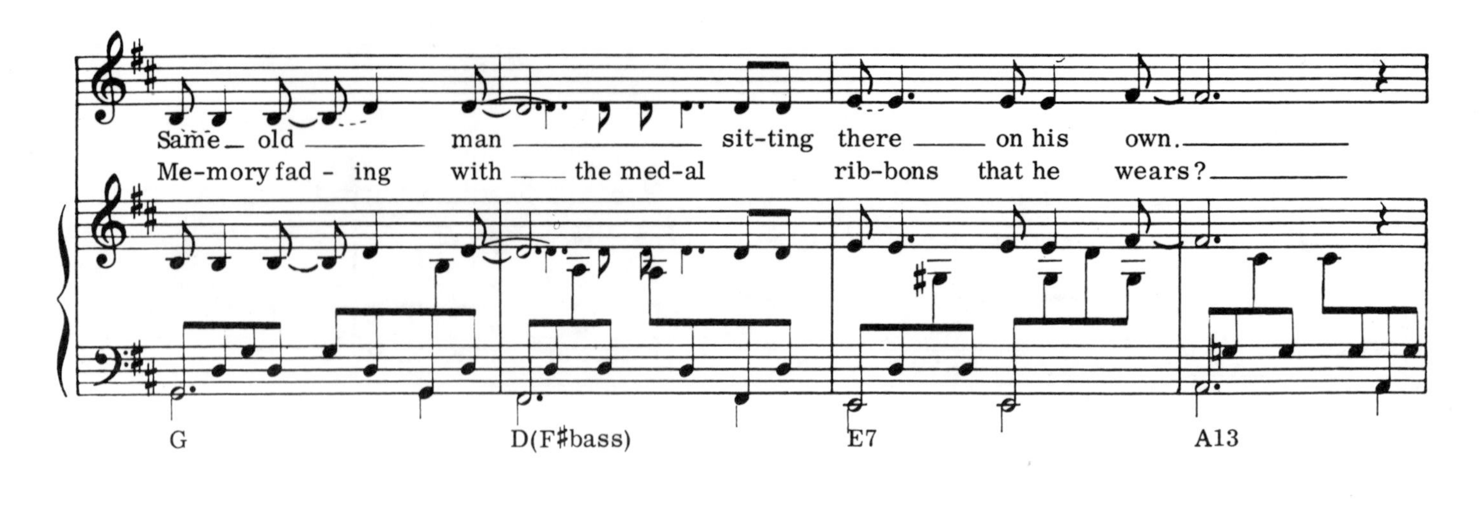
Same old man sitting there on his own.
Me-mory fad-ing with the med-al rib-bons that he wears?
G
D(F#bass)
E7
A13

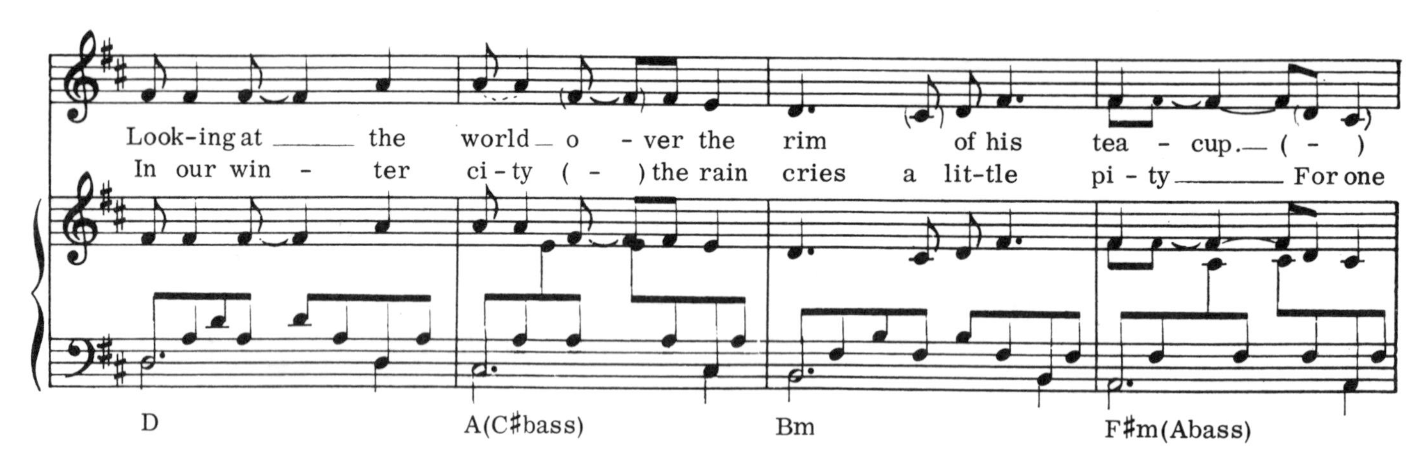
Look-ing at the world o-ver the rim of his tea-cup. (-)
In our win-ter ci-ty (-) the rain cries a lit-tle pi-ty For one
D
A(C#bass)
Bm
F#m(Abass)

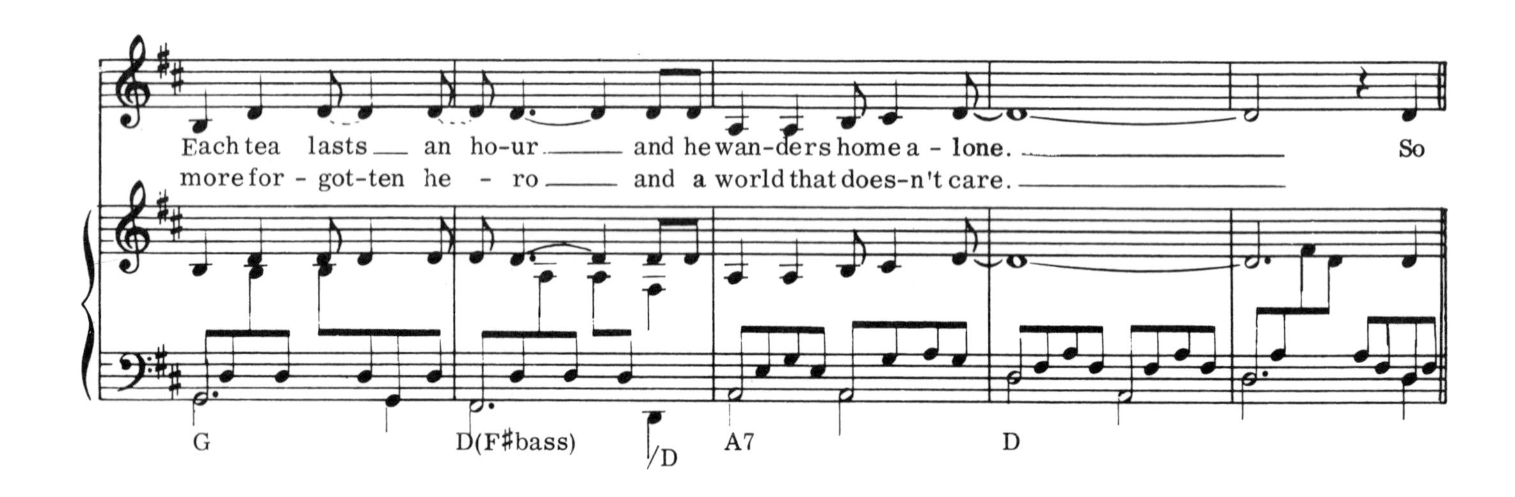
Each tea lasts an hour and he wan-ders home a-lone. So
more for-got-ten he-ro and a world that does-n't care.
G
D(F#bass)
/D
A7
D

CHORUS
how can you tell me you're lone ly
G
D
D/F#
A7
Bm
Bm7/A

And say for you — that the sun don't shine? —
E7/G#
A7

Let me take — you by the hand — and lead you through — the streets of Lon - don.
D
A(C#bass)
Bm
F#m(Abass)

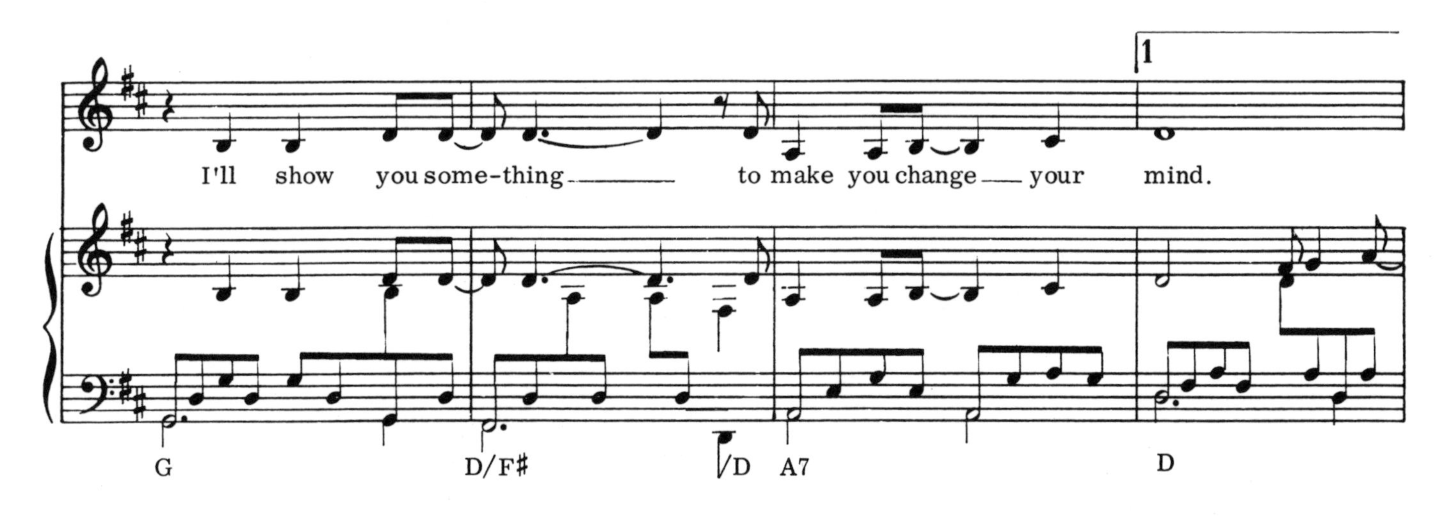
1
I'll show you some-thing — to make you change — your mind.
G
D/F#
/D
A7
D

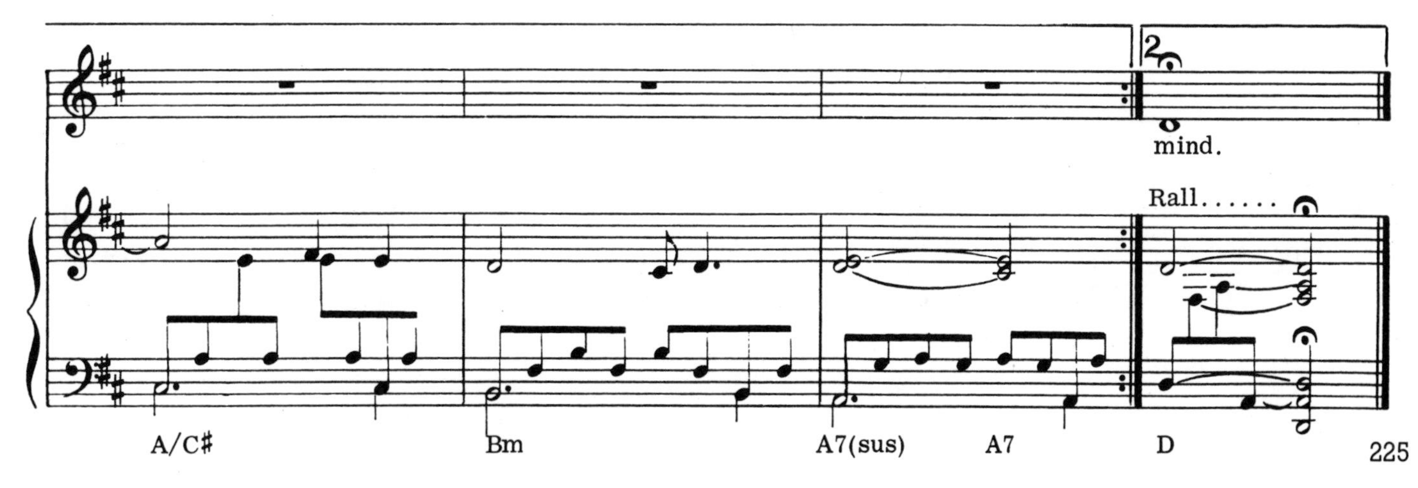
2
mind.
Rall......
A/C#
Bm
A7(sus)
A7
D

HELP ME MAKE IT THROUGH THE NIGHT

Words & Music: Kris Kristofferson

1.
D
G
like the shad - ows on the wall.
2.-3.
A7
D
G
HELP ME MAKE IT THROUGH THE NIGHT,
D
G
I don't care who's right or wrong;
D
I don't try to un - der - stand;

3. Yesterday is dead and gone,
And tomorrow's out of sight;
And it's sad to be alone;
HELP ME MAKE IT THROUGH THE NIGHT.

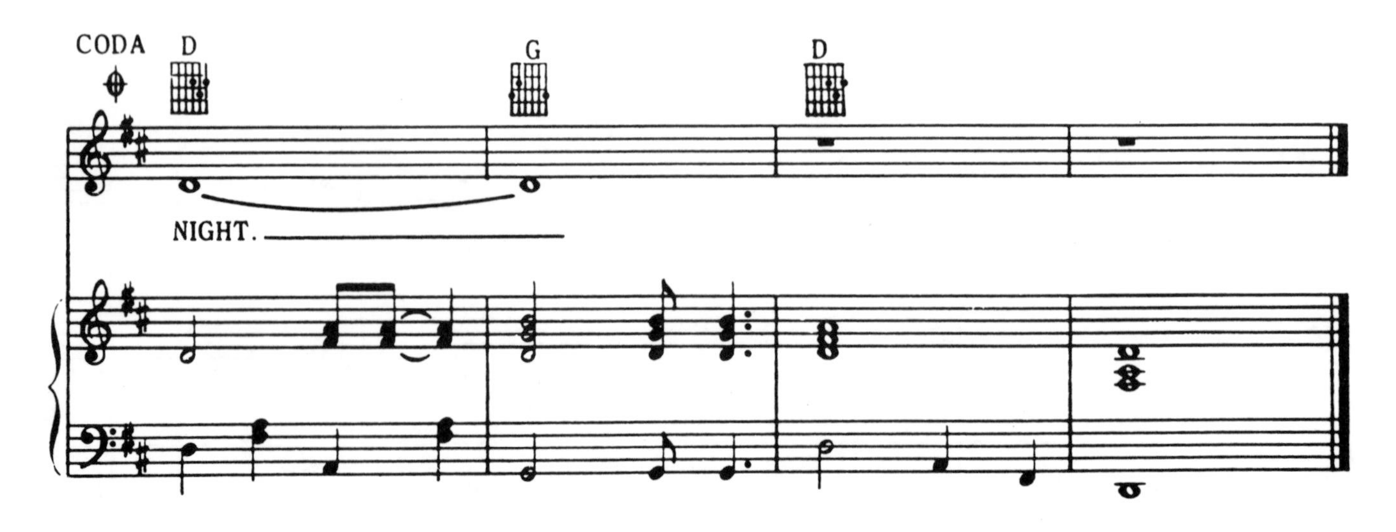

I CAN SEE CLEARLY NOW

Words & Music: Johnny Nash

To Coda ⊕
G
D
C
bright — sun shin-y day, —
It's gon-na be a bright,
G
D
bright — sun shin - y day. —
F
C
Look all a - round — there's noth-ing but blue sky, —
cresc.
F
A
G
F
A
Look straight a-head — noth - ing but blue sky. —

D♭m
G
D♭m
G
C
D6 (omit 5th)
A
poco dim.
D. S. al Coda
CODA
D
C
G
It's gon-na be a bright, bright— sun shin- y day.-
1
D
2
D

YOU LIGHT UP MY LIFE

Words & Music: Joe Brooks

G
B♭7
Fm7
B♭7
lone in the dark, but now you've come a - long.
nev - er a - gain to be all a - lone
And
rit.
cresc.
E♭
E♭maj7
E♭7
C7
you light up my life. You give me hope,
f
Fm
Fm7
B♭7
To Coda
to car - ry on. You light up my days and fill my
1. E♭
B♭
(D Bass)
Cm
Fm
B♭7
nights with song.
mf

2.
E♭
B♭
(D Bass)
Cm
Fm
B♭
D.S. al Coda
nights with song.
cresc.
G
Cm
F
E♭
(B♭ Bass)
nights with song. It can't be wrong when
Coda
f
G
Cm
F
E♭
(B♭ Bass)
Fm
(B♭ Bass)
it feels so right, 'cause you
mf
decresc.
B♭
A♭
E♭
B♭
A♭
E♭
you light up my life.
mp
mf
rit.
f

I WRITE THE SONGS

Words & Music: Bruce Johnston

CHORUS
songs.
old.
I write the songs that make the whole world sing,
Eb11
Eb7
Ab
Bbm7
I write the songs of love and special things.
Eb7
Eb11
Eb7
Db/Ab
Ab
I write the songs that make those young girls cry,
Fm
Bbm7
Bb7
1
(and for repeat last time)
2
I write the songs, I write the songs.
Eb11
Eb7
Ab
Ab
Db/Ab

Oh my mus-ic makes you dance gives you spirit to take a chance,
Dbm/Ab Ab G(sus 4) G Gm G(sus4)
and I wrote some rock 'n' roll so you'd feel so good, my
C C6 Cmaj7 C
mus - ic's in your heart and it's a real fine place to start it's from me
Bb11 Bb Eb11 Bb
D.S. (repeat Chorus ad-lib. and fade)
ten.
It's through you, it's from you, it's through me, it's a world_ wide sym-pho - ny.
molto rit.
Bbm7/Eb Eb7 Eb Bbm7/Eb Gbmaj7 Eb7/G

BRIGHT EYES

Words & Music: Mike Batt

G
C
Am7
D
death down-stream
oh is it a dream?
hills un - seen
or is it a dream?
D7
G
C
G
There's a fog a - long the hor - i - zon
There's a high wind in the trees
Em
C
G
a strange glow in the sky
and
a cold sound in the air
and
D
D/C
G
C
no - bo - dy seems to know where you go
and what does it
no - bo - dy ev - er knows when you go
and where do you

B/D♯
C♯dim
G/D
D7
G
mean
start
Oh
oh
oh
oh
is it a
in-to the
dream?
dark.
CHORUS
Bm
C
D7
Bright eyes
burn-ing like fire,
Bm
C
Bright eyes
how can you close and fail
Am
B7/D♯
Em
D7/F♯
G
How can the light that burned so bright-ly

C
1 Am
D7
G
sud-den-ly burn so pale?
Bright eyes.
Em
C
2 Am
D7
To Coda
G
D.%. (no repeat) al Coda
bright eyes,
Bright eyes.
CODA
G
poco rit.

JUST THE WAY YOU ARE

Words & Music: Billy Joel

Bm7
E9
A9sus
E bass
And I don't see you any more
D
Bm6
Gmaj7
I would not leave you in times of
Bm
D7
Gmaj7
Gm
trou-ble We nev-er could have come this far
D
F♯bass
Am
D7
Gmaj7
Gm6
mm mm I took the good times

D
F♯bass
Bm7
Em7
I'll take the bad times
I'll take you just
A9sus
D
Gm
G
D bass
D
the way you are
Gm6
G
D bass
D
Bm6
Don't go try-ing
Gmaj7
Bm
D7
Gmaj7
Some new fash - ion
Don't change the col -

Gm
D
F♯bass
Am7
D7
Gmaj7
— or of your hair —
mm — mm — You al - ways
Gm
D
F♯bass
Bm7
have my un - spok - en pas - sion —
E9sus
E9
A9sus
Al - though I might — not seem to care —
D
Bm6
Gmaj7
— I — don't — want clev - er — con - ver-

Bm
D7
Gmaj7
Gm
D
F♯bass
sa-tion
I nev-er want to work that hard
Am7
D7
Gmaj7
Gm
D
F♯bass
mm mm I just want some-one that I can talk
Bm7
Em7
A9 sus
to I want you just the way you are.
D
Gm6
D bass
G
D
D bass
Gm6
D bass
D
D7

G
A
F#m7
B7
I need to know that you will al - ways be
Em7
A
D
Am
C bass
The same old some - one that I knew
Oh
Bb
C
Am7
What will it take till you be - lieve in me
D
D7
Gm7
C
The way that I be - lieve in you

A9sus
D
Bm6
voice tacet on D. S.
I said I love you
instrumental on D. S.
Gmaj7
Bm
D7
Gmaj7
Gm
Gm6
and that's for-ev - er
And this I prom-ise from the heart
D
F♯bass
Am7
D7
Gmaj7
Gm6
mm mm I could not love you
D
F♯bass
Bm7
Em7
an - y bet-ter
I love you just
248

A9 sus
D
Gm6
G
D bass
D
Gm6
the way you are
G
D bass
D
D. S. al Coda
Coda
D
E bass
E9
A9 sus
D
Bm6
I don't want clev-er
G7
Bm
D7
Gmaj7
con - ver-sa - tion
I nev-er

Gm
D
F♯bass
Am7
D7
Gmaj7
want_ to work_ that hard_
mm
I just want
Gm6
D
F♯bass
Bm7
Em7
some-one_
that I can talk_ to_
I want you just_
G
A bass
B♭
C
Am7
_ the way you are
D7
Gm7
A7
Dmaj7
Whoa

BRIDGE OVER TROUBLED WATER

Words & Music: Paul Simon

Eb
Ab
Eb
Bb
Cm
Bb
I'm on your side. Oh,
I'll take your part. Oh,
mp
Bb9
Eb
Eb (D bass)
In tempo
Eb7
Eb9
Ab
F
when times get rough
when dark - ness comes
And friends just can't be found,
And pain is all a - round,
f
Bb
Eb7
Eb9
Ab
F#dim (A bass)
Eb (Bb bass)
C7sus
C7
Like a Bridge O - ver Trou-bled Wa - ter
mp
Ab
G7
Cm
Eb7
Eb9
Ab
F#dim (A bass)
1. Eb (Bb bass)
C7sus
C7
I will lay me down. Like a Bridge O - ver Trou-bled Wa - ter
mf
mp

Ab
Bb9 (sus)
Bb7
Eb
Ab
I will lay me down.
mf
f
Eb
Ab
Eb
Ab
Rubato
When you're
mf
mp
mf
mp
p
2
Eb (Bb bass)
Cm
Ab
Cm (G bass)
G
Cm
F7
Trou-bled Wa-ter I will lay me down.
mf
f
Eb
Ab
Cm
Ab
Abm
Eb

Ab
Eb
Ab
Eb
Ab
Sail on
Eb
sil - ver girl,
Sail on by.
Ab
Db
Ab
Your time has
Eb
Ab
come to shine.
Eb
Ab
All your dreams are on their way.
Eb
Ab
Eb
Bb
Cm
Bb
See how they shine.
Oh,
Eb
if you need
Eb (D bass)
a friend
mp

In tempo
Eb7
Eb9
Ab
F
Bb
Eb7
Eb9
Ab
F#dim (A bass)
I'm sail - ing right be - hind. Like a Bridge O - ver
f
Eb (Bb bass)
Cm
Ab
Cm
G
Cm
Eb7
Eb9
Ab
Abmaj7
F7 (A bass)
Trou-bled Wa-ter I will ease your mind. Like a Bridge O - ver
mf
f
ff
Eb (Bb bass)
Cm
Ab
G7
Cm
F9
Fmaj9
Trou - bled Wa-ter I will ease your mind.
Eb (Bb bass)
Ab
Abm
Eb
rall.
fff

CAN'T SMILE WITHOUT YOU

Words & Music: Chris Arnold,
David Martin & Geoff Morrow

G
Em
feel sad when you're sad. I feel glad when you're glad. If
Am
C/D
you on-ly knew what I'm go-ing through; I just can't smile with-out
G
C/D
G(addA)
G
Em7
you. You came a-long just like a song and
Am7
C/D
D7
G(addA)
G
bright-ened my day. Who'd-a be-lieved that you were part of a dream.

Em7
Am7
D7
C/E
D7/F♯
3 fr.
Now it all seems light-years a - way. And now you know I
G
Em
can't smile with - out you. I can't smile with - out you. I
Am
C/D
can't laugh and I can't sing. I'm find - ing it hard_ to
D♭/E♭
A♭
4 fr.
do an - y - thing._ You see, I feel sad when you're sad.
cresc.
mf

Fm
B♭m
I feel glad when you're glad. If you_ on-ly knew what I'm_ go-ing through;
D♭/E♭
E♭m7
6 fr.
I just can't smile._ Now, some peo-ple say_ hap-pi-ness takes_
E♭m7/A♭
D♭maj7
4 fr.
D♭m(maj7)
4 fr.
so_ ver-y long to find._ Well, I'm find-ing it hard_ leav-ing your love be-hind_
E♭7sus4
6 fr.
E7sus4
7 fr.
A
_ me. And you see, I can't smile with-out you.
cresc.
f

F♯m
Bm
I can't smile with - out you. I can't laugh and I can't sing. I'm
D/E
E♭/F
B♭
Repeat and fade
find-ing it hard to do an - y - thing._You see, I feel glad when
you.
cresc.
ff
Repeat and fade
Gm
3 fr.
Cm
3 fr.
you're glad. I feel sad when you're sad. If you _ on - ly knew what
Instrumental till fade
E♭/F
I'm _ go - ing through; I just can't smile with-out

MY SWEET LORD

Words & Music: George Harrison

E
C♯m
4fr.
see you. Real-ly want to be with you. Real-ly want to
know you. Real-ly want to go with you. Real-ly want to
E♯°7
C♯7
F♯m
B
see you, Lord, but it takes so long, my Lord.
show you, Lord, that it won't take long, my Lord.
My sweet Lord, mm my Lord,
My sweet Lord, mm my Lord,
mm my Lord, I real-ly want to
my sweet Lord, I real-ly want to see you.

E7
C#7
4fr.
Real-ly want to see you.
Real-ly want to see_ you, Lord._
F#
Fx°7
D#7
6fr.
Real-ly want to see you, Lord,_but it takes_ so long_ my Lord,_
G#m
C#m
C#
_ my ___ sweet Lord, _ mm___ my_ Lord,_
D. S. 𝄋 and fade
_ my, my,_ my Lord,_ my _ sweet Lord,_

SOMETHING

Words & Music: George Harrison

A
Amaj7
F♯m
You're ask - ing me will my love grow.
I don't know,
D
G
A
I don't know.
A
Amaj7
F♯m
A
You stick a - round now, it may show,
I don't know,
D
G
C
I don't know.

C
Cmaj7
C7
Some-thing in the way she knows
And all I have to do is
F
D
D7
G
think of her,
Some-thing in the things she shows me.
I
Am
Am(♯7)
Am7
D9
don't want to leave her now,
You know I be-lieve and how.
F
E♭
G
A
F
E♭
G
C

Girl's Names

SWEET LEILANI

Words & Music: Harry Owens

F
Bb
Bbm
SWEET LEI-LA-NI, Heav-en-ly Flow - er,
F
C7
F
C7
F
Trop-ic skies are jeal-ous as they shine,
I think they're jeal-ous of your blue eyes,
C7
F
Bb
Bbm
Jeal-ous be-cause you're mine; SWEET LEI-LA-NI, Heav-en-ly Flow - er,
F
C7
F
C7
F
I dreamed of par-a-dise for two,
You are my par-a-dise com-plet-ed,
C7
F
You are my dream come true.
p (quasi echo)

ANNIE'S SONG

Words & Music: John Denver

A7
G
rain, Like a storm in the des -
A
Bm
G
D
D/C♯
ert, like a sleep - y blue o - cean,
D/B
D/A
G
F♯m
Em
You fill up my sen - ses, come
A7
D
Dsus4
D
Dsus4
fill me a - gain. Come let me

G
A
Bm
G
love you, let me give my life
sen - ses like a night in a
D
D/C♯
D/B
D/A
G
to you, Let me drown in your laugh -
for - est, Like the moun - tains in spring -
F♯m
Em
G
A7
ter, let me die in your arms.
time, like a walk in the rain.
G
A
Bm
Let me lay down be - side you, let me
Like a storm in the des - ert, like a
2nd time hold back---

G
D
D/C♯
D/B
al - ways be with you,
sleep - y blue o - cean,
You
in tempo
D/A
G
F♯m
Em
A7
Come let me love you, come love me a -
fill up my sen - ses, come fill me a -
1.
D
Dsus4
D
Dsus4
gain. You fill up my
2.
D
gain.
dim.
Dsus4
D
Dsus4
D
Dsus4
D

CECILIA

Words & Music: Paul Simon

F Bb F C F
(mak - ing love)
- lia, Up in my bed - room, I got up to wash
Bb F C F
my face When I come back to bed, some-one's tak - en my place.
F Bb F Bb F
Cel - ia, You're break-ing my heart, You're shak-ing my con - fi - dence dai -
mf
C Bb F Bb F
- ly. Oh, Ce - cil - ia, I'm down on my knees, I'm
Bb F C F
beg-ging you please to come home. Come on home. Poh poh
mp
mf

Fsus
F
B♭
C
poh poh poh poh poh poh poh poh poh poh poh. Ju-bi-
f
B♭ F B♭ F B♭ F
la-tion, She loves me a-gain, I fall on the floor and I laugh-
f
mf
1. C
-ing. Ju-bi-
2. C
-ing. Oh oh oh oh oh
B♭ F
oh oh oh oh oh oh oh oh oh oh oh oh.
B♭ F
1. C
Oh oh
2. C
oh. Come on home.
mf
rall.

PEARL'S A SINGER

Words & Music: Ralph Dino, John Sembello, Jerry Leiber & Mike Stoller

and the lone - ly.
Her job is
cut a re - cord.
They played it
F
en - ter - tain - ing folks,
sing - ing songs
and tell - ing jokes
for a week
or so
on the lo - cal ra - di - o,
G
Dm7
F
To Coda
in a night - club.
Pearl's a
it ne - ver
made it.
C
F/C
C
tacet . . . . *
She want - ed to be Bet - ty Gra - ble
G

but now she sits there at that beer - stained
G/B Am D G11 G
ta - ble — dream - ing of the things — she nev - er got to do, —
G11 F E Am G
— all those dreams — that nev - er — came true.
F D7 G11 G7 C F/C
D. S. al Coda
CODA
Pearl's a
night - club. ——
rall.
C tacet- - - - -*
C F C

CLAIR

Words & Music: Raymond O'Sullivan

mo-ment I met you a - gain I knew in my heart that we were
ev - er a mo ment so rare was cap-tured for all to com-
Bbm7 m9 m7 Eb9 13 9 Cm7
friends, it had to be so, it could - n't be no; But
-pare that mo - ment is you, in all that you do; But
Fm Bbm7 Gm7(b5) Eb7
try as hard as I might do I don't know why,
why in spite of our age dif - f'rence do I cry
3
Ab Ab4 Ab F#dim Bbm7
you get to me in a way I can't des-cribe,
each time I leave you I feel I could die,
Words mean so lit tle when you
No-thing means more to me than
Eb7 Abmaj7 Dbmaj7

look up and smile I don't care what peo-ple say to me, you're
hear-ing you say I'm going to mar - ry you, will you mar - ry
B♭9
A♭6
Dal 𝄋 al Coda
more than a child oh Clair
me Un-cle Ray oh Clair
Clair
Clair
B♭9
B♭m7
E♭9 4 13
E♭9
CODA
Solo
F♯m7
Bm7
E7
Amaj7
D♯m7(♭5)
C♯maj7

Clair
I've told you be- fore, don't you
C#maj7
Fm7
m9
m7
Bbm9
Bbm7
dare
get
back
in -to
bed,
can't you
see
that it's
late,
no you can't
Eb13
b9
Abmaj7
Fm7
Bbm7
Eb9
have a
drink;
Oh
al
-
right
then
but
wait
just
a
bit
Abmaj7
Fm7
Bbm7
Eb9
while
I
in
an
ef
-
fort
to
ba-by
sit
Ab
Ab4
Ab
F#dim
Bbm7

cap-ture my breath, what there is left of it.
You can be mur der at this
Eb7
Abmaj7
Dbmaj7
hour of the day, but in the morn - ing, to - night will seem a
Bb9
Ab6
life-time a-way, Oh Clair Clair Clair
rall
Bb9
Bbm7
Eb9 4 13
Eb9
Dm7(b5)
Oh Clair.
poco a poco
Dbmaj7
Ab
Bbm7
Eb13 Eb7
Abmaj7

LAURA

Words: Johnny Mercer
Music: David Raksin

Slowly with expression
Chorus
Am7
D7-9
G
Lau - ra is the face in the mist - y light
mp
Gm7
C7-9
Fmaj7
F6
Foot - steps that you hear down the hall
Fm7
Ab m6
Bb 7-9
Eb maj7
Eb
The laugh that floats on a sum - mer night That you can
Cm6
D7-9 -5
4 fr.
D9-5
D7
Bm
G
E9
E7-9
Am7
nev - er quite re - call And you see Lau - ra

D7-9
G
Gm7
on the train that is pass - ing thru
Those eyes
C7-9
Fmaj7
F6
Fm7
how fa - mil - iar they seem
She gave
Fdim
C
D7
D7-9 -5 4 fr.
D7-9 +5 4 fr.
your ver - y first kiss to you
That was Lau - ra
G9
G7-9
1. C
E9
E7-9
2. C
but she's on - ly a dream.
dream.
rall.
p

ELEANOR RIGBY

Words & Music: John Lennon
& Paul McCartney

C
wear-ing the face ___ that she keeps ___ in a jar ___ by the door, ___
darn-ing his socks ___ in the night ___ when there's no - bod - y there, ___
wip-ing the dirt ___ from his hands ___ as he walks ___ from the grave, ___
Em
Em7
Em6
C
who is it for?
what does he care?
no one was saved.
All the lone - ly peo - ple, where do ___ they all ___ come from? ___
Em
Em7
Em6
C
To Coda
All the lone - ly peo - ple, where do ___ they all ___ be-long? ___
To Coda
Em
Em
1.
2.
D.C. al Coda
Coda
Em

MICHELLE

Words & Music: John Lennon
& Paul McCartney

Cm F7 B♭ A Dm Gm
That's all I want to say. Un-til I find a way I will
I need to make you see what you mean to me. Un-
I think you know by now. I'll get to you some-how. Un-
Dm C♯+ Dm7 Dm6 Gm6 A A
To Coda
1. 2.
D. S. al ⊕ Coda
say the on-ly words I know that you'll, un-der-stand.
til I do, I'm hop-ing you will know what I mean. I
til I do, I'm tell-ing you, so you'll un-der-
Coda
A D Gm B♭ C B♭
stand. Mi-chelle ma belle sont les mots qui vont tres bien en-
mf
A B♭ A B♭ Dm Gm
semble, tres bien en-semble. I will say the on-ly words I know that you'll un-der-
A D Gm7 C7 B♭ A
stand, my Mi-chelle.

BALLADE POUR ADELINE

Composer: Paul de Senneville

F
G4/7
G7
8ve
G
C
B
Dm
G7
C
E♭
F
G
C
Dm7
G7
C
1
To A
2
To B
3
rall.
C
F
G
C
F
G
C
F
G
C

ONCE IN LOVE WITH AMY

Words & Music: Frank Loesser

Am7 D7 Em7 A7 D7
boom, boom, boom, boom, boom, Boom, boom, boom, boom from then on, For
Chorus
G G#dim D7 G G#dim D7
ONCE IN LOVE WITH A-MY, Al-ways in love with A-my.
mp
G G7 C G Am7 G A7 D7♭9 D7
Ev-er and ev-er fas-cin-at-ed by 'er, Sets your heart a-fire to stay.
G G#dim D7 G G#dim D7
Once you're kissed by A-my, Tear up your list, it's A-my.
G G7 C G Am7 G B7 E7♭9 E7
Ply her with bon-bons, po-et-ry and flow-ers, Moon a mil-lion hours a-way. You

Am7 D9 Gmaj7 C9 Gmaj7 C9 Gmaj7 E9 E7
might be quite the fick-le-heart-ed ro - ver, So care - free and bold Who
Am7 D9 Gmaj7 C9 D A7 D7
loves a girl and la-ter thinks it o - ver And just quits cold, But
mf
G G♯dim D7 G G♯dim D7 G G7
ONCE IN LOVE WITH A-MY, Al-ways in love with A - my. Ev-er and ev-er
mp
C G Am7 G B7 E7♭9 E7 Am7
sweet-ly you'll ro-mance 'er. Trou-ble is, the an-swer will be That A - my'd rath-er stay in
A9 D7 1 G Am7 D7 2 G
love with me. me.
mf
p

Love
Songs

UNFORGETTABLE

Words & Music: Irving Gordon

Un-for-get-ta-ble in ev-'ry way,
G
Gdim
C
And for ev-er-more that's how you'll stay. That's why, dar-ling,
C
A9 Em7 Cm A9 F
it's in-cred-i-ble, That some-one so Un-for-get-ta-ble Thinks that I am
Fm C Gm6 A7 D7
1
2
Un-for-get-ta-ble too. too.
mf
G7 C C♯7 D7 C♯7 Am7 D7 C Dm7 D♭7 C6

BECAUSE OF YOU

Words & Music: Arthur Hammerstein
& Dudley Wilkinson

Bb7 Fm Ab6 Bb7 Eb Eb Bb+ Bbm6 C7
You my ro-mance had its start. Be-cause Of You the sun will shine, the moon and
Fm C7-9 Fm F9 F7-9 Fm7 Abm6 Bb7 Gm C#dim
stars will say you're mine for-ev-er and nev-er to part. I on-ly
Bb7 Fm Ab6 Bb7 Eb Eb Bb+ Bbm6 C7 Bbm C7
live for your love and your kiss. It's par-a-dise to be near you like
Fm C7 Fm Ab D7 Eb Cm G7 Cm7
this. Be-cause Of You my life is now worth while; and I can
F9 Bb7 1. Eb B7 Bb7 Gm6 C#dim 2. Eb Ab6 Eb6
smile, Be-cause Of You. Be-cause Of You.
rall

LOVE ME TENDER

Words & Music: Elvis Presley
& Vera Matson

life com - plete, And I love you so.
I be - long, And we'll nev - er part.
all the years, Till the end of time.
fol - low you Ev - 'ry - where you go
A7
D7 sus4
D7
G
CHORUS
Love me ten - der, love me true, All my dreams ful -
mf
G
B7
Em
G7
C
Cm
- fill For, my dar - lin', I love you,
G
G
Dm6
E7+
E7
A7
1
2
And I al - ways will. And I al - ways will.
D7 sus4
D7
G
Am7
D7
D7 sus4
D7
G

TOGETHER

Words & Music: C. Fox & N. Gimbel

F
C9
F
Dm
F
be. To-geth-er, To-geth-er, heed-less of
May. But, now in De-cem-ber, love is an
Dm6
A
E7
A
C7
Gm7
D♭dim
weath-er, Now there is on-ly me, dear.
em-ber, 'Cause you have gone a-way, dear.
mf
rit.
Refrain (slowly)
C7
C+
We strolled the lane, to-geth-er; Laughed at the rain, to-
p
L.H.
D7
Gm
geth-er, Sang love's re-frain, to-geth-er. And we'd
We knew
L.H.
L.H.

G7
Bbm6
F
both pre - tend, It would nev - er end. One day we cried, to-
long a - go, That our love would grow. Through storm and sun to-
rit.
a tempo
C7
D7
Gm
geth - er, Cast love a - side to - geth - er.
geth - er, Our hearts as one to - geth - er.
L.H.
L.H.
Ped.
Ped.
E7
F6
C+
Bb+
D7+
D7
Gm
You're gone from me; But in my mem - o - ry, We al - ways will
mf
rit.
p a tempo
1.
2.
Gm7
C9
F
C9
C7-9
Gm7
C7
F
be to - geth - er.
be to - geth - er.
rit.
mf

THERE I'VE SAID IT AGAIN

Words & Music: Redd Evans & Dave Mann

Bb9 Bb+ Eb Bb6/D Bbdim Bb6 F7
more can I say? Be - lieve me, there's no oth-er way. I love you no
Fm6 G+ G7 C9 Cm7 Ebm6 F7 F7+ Bb Bbmaj7 F+
use to pre-tend. There! I've said it a - gain. I've said it. There's
Bb9 Bb+ Eb Bb6/D Bbdim Bb6 F7
no-thing to hide. It's bet-ter than burn-ing in - side. I love you. I
Fm6 G+ G7 C9 Cm7 F9 Bb Bb+ Gm Fm7 Bb7
will to the end. There! I've said it a - gain. I've tried to drum up a

Fm7 Bb7 Eb6 Gm Bb+ Eb Ebmaj7 Eb7 Gm7 C7
phrase that would sum up all that I feel for you. But what good are phras-es? The
Gm7 C7 F9sus4 F7+(b9) Bb Bbmaj7 F+
thought that a-maz-es is you love me, and it's hea-ven-ly. For-give me for
Bb9 Bb+ Eb Bb6/D Bbdim Bb6 F7
want-ing you so, but one thing I want you to know, I've loved you since
Fm6 G+ 1st Fret G7 C9 Cm7 F9 1 Bb Gm Bb+ Bb F7+ 2 Bb Eb6 Bb6
hea-ven knows when. There! I've said it a-gain. I've

STRANGERS IN THE NIGHT

Words: Charles Singleton & Eddie Snyder
Music: Bert Kaempfert

Something in your smile was so ex-cit-ing, Some-thing in my heart
Told me I must have you.
Strangers in the night,
Two lone-ly peo-ple we were strangers in the night,
Up to the moment when we said our first hel-lo,
Lit-tle did we know
Love was just a glance a-way. a
C9
Gm7
C7
F
Am7♭5
D7♭9
Gm
Gm7♭5
F
Dm7
rit.

warm em-bracing dance a-way and ev-er since that night we've been to-geth-er,
Gm7 C7 F
a tempo
Lov-ers at first sight, In love for-ev-er, It turned out so right,
C9
For strangers in the night.
1
Gm7 C7 F Gm7 C9
2
night.
rit.
F Gm7 Fmaj7 F7 F6

THIS GUY'S IN LOVE WITH YOU

Words: Hal David
Music: Burt Bacharach

G7(sus) G9 G7 Cm7 B♭m7
looks at you the way I do? When you smile,
mp
E♭9(sus) E♭7 A♭maj7 A♭m6
I can tell we know each oth - er ver - y well. How
p
Gm7 Cm7 Fm9
Steady
can I show you I'm glad I
cresc. poco a poco
B♭9(sus) E♭ A♭maj7
got to know you,'cause I've heard some talk. They
2nd time fade out within ten measures
f p

D♭maj7
E♭
say you think I'm fine.
This guy's in love,
A♭maj7
G7(sus)
G9
G7
Cm7
and what I'd do to make you mine.
B♭m7
E♭9(sus)
E♭7
A♭maj7
Tell me now, is it so? Don't let me be the
mp
A♭m6
Gm7
Cm7
last to know. My hands are shak - ing. Don't
p
cresc. poco a poco

Fm9
B♭ 9 (sus)
E♭
Majestically
A♭ maj7
let my heart keep break - ing, 'cause I need your love.
ff
E♭
A♭ maj7
I want your love.
E♭
Broadly
Dm7
Cm7
Cm6
Cm7
F7
Say you're in love, in love with this
f
B♭
B maj7
B♭ 7
(Tacet) ad lib.
D.S. for fade out
guy. If not, I'll just die.
ff
p colla voce

DAYS OF WINE AND ROSES

Words: Johnny Mercer
Music: Henry Mancini

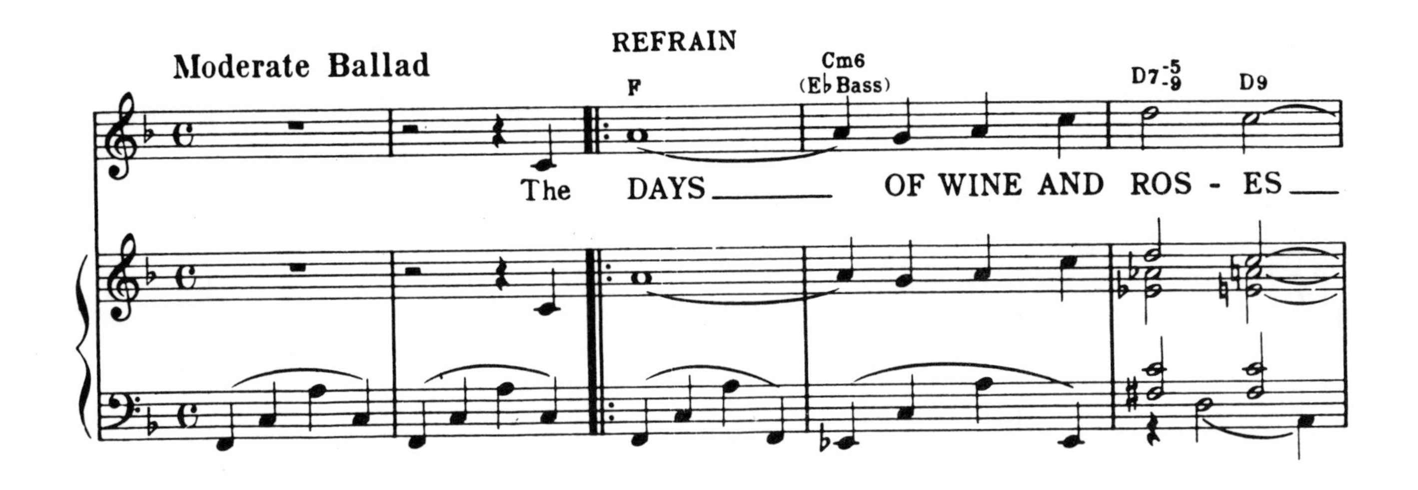

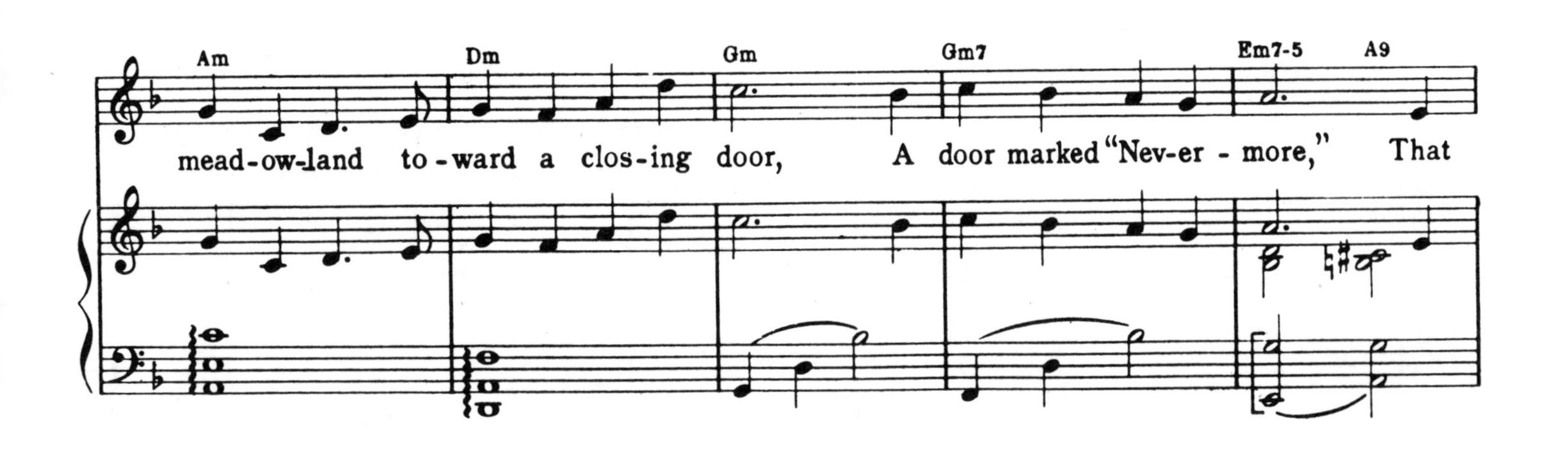

Dm7-5 G9 Gm7 C7 F Cm6 (Eb Bass)
was-n't there be-fore. The lone - ly night dis-
D7 -5 -9 D9 Gm Bbn
clos - es Just a pass-ing breeze Filled with mem-o-ries
Bbm Am Dm Dm7 Bm7-5 Bb9
Of the gold-en smile that in-tro-duced me to The
Am Dm Gm7 1. F F° Gm7 C7 2. F Gm7 F
DAYS OF WINE AND ROS-ES and you. The you.
rall.

I WILL WAIT FOR YOU

Words: Normal Gimbel
Music: Michel Legrand

1.
Dm Gm6 A+ A7
arms. An - y
2. Ahead to Interlude
Dm Gm6 Dm
you. The
3.
Dm Gm6 Dm
love.
Fine
Interlude
Bb Gm
clock will tick a-way the hours one by one and
Bb Dm Bb Dm Bb
then the time will come when all the wait - ing's done. The
Gm6 A79b Bm75b Bb7
time when you re - turn and find me here and run, Straight
A7 Em75b Bm7 Bb75b A7 rit.
to my wait - ing arms. If it
rit.